A DOCTOR IS BORN

By W. D. Chesney, M. D.

Milton Junction, Wisconsin, 1958

Printed In The United States

First Edition

This book is dedicated to all those engaged in the art of healing, according to their conscience and their Hippocratic Oath, in servitude only to the sick, and without bigotry or intolerance, to the honor and glory of their profession.

CHAPTER 1

The cold metallic *click* of a revolver being cocked brought the boy's startled eyes up from the book he had been reading. All that day, and all the other days running back at least seven of his sixteen years, his parents had been in continuous wordy strife. Accustomed to this never-ending battle, he had not really been paying any attention to the charges and counter-charges of drunkenness and adultery, but now he looked up in alarm, latently aware of the words his father had just spoken, and which he was now repeating.

"I'm getting out of here! I'm sick and tired of your infernal, eternal nagging!"

His father, a packed Gladstone bag in his right hand, stood near the door. Apparently he had made up his mind at last to carry out his oft-repeated threat to desert his family.

His mother stood like a statue. The .45 Colt she held in her right hand rose slowly until it pointed straight between his father's eyes. She was as steady as the Rock of Gibraltar, although her deep bosom rose and fell in a far more tumultuous manner than any Hollywood tragedienne. She said in a restrained, cold voice: "John Marsh, I gave up my family and friends to marry you. I have helped make a living for us. If you think you are running out on us now, you had better make another guess. Don't reach for that door knob, or it will be the last thing you will ever touch. I mean it. I have put up with your philandering for eighteen years – but no more! You stay here, or die!"

His father sneered. "You haven't the intestines to shoot a mouse! Ever since those cursed surgeons took them out, you have been nothing but a block of ice. I'm leaving with Mabel Scott on No. 10."

His mother's eyes were now mere slits. Her hand, holding death, was steady. "John," she repeated, "don't even touch that door knob. I warn you!"

The boy screamed in mental anguish. "Mother, for God's sake, don't do it! Please, if you care anything about me, don't kill Dad! They will take you to prison, and what will become of me?"

"Don't fear, Johnny," sneered his father. "She won't shoot." He reached out his hand and grasped the door knob, leering at his wife. "Well, why don't you shoot? Damned slut! I dare you!"

Three sharp reports rang out and John Marsh dropped to the floor. The new-made widow turned the gun and pressed it to her breast. A muted report, and she, too, dropped to the floor. She had not struck the heart, but the blood poured from her in a flood.

John Marsh, aged 16, ran over to her and tried in anguished panic to stop the hemorrhage with her handkerchief. His mother shook her head weakly and gasped: "No use, Johnny, I'm dying. You've always wanted to be a doctor – in the safe you'll find two insurance policies that will educate you and set you up in practice. Goodbye, son; try to be something your father was not – an honest, decent man." She gasped faintly and was gone.

Neighbors came rushing in, doctors were called, then the coroner. Finally the mortician.

John Marsh, Jr., was taken to live with his mother's parents. All that following night the boy raved as one who had lost his mind. The awful execution of his father by his mother, and then her suicide before his eyes had been altogether too much for his nervous system and he, for the time being at least, was nearer death than he had ever been before, or probably ever would be again until he at last was to meet the grim reaper face to face. He went into a state of profound melancholia that the doctor who had been called in to treat him could not control.

Finally, as a last resort, a physician of the old school, a country general practitioner whose first thought was to help his patients before thinking of the patient's financial standing, was called in to take full charge of young John Marsh, and from that day the lad began to start back toward health. This old G.P., unlike most of the modern young doctors, did not permit the representatives of great pharmaceutical houses to tell him how to practice the healing art. Nor had he ever used the highly over-advertised German, or American, synthetic drugs made from the refuse of the coal pit, or the oil well.

He believed that Nature's God had furnished, in botanical products, a remedy for every disease to which the flesh is heir. Furthermore, he often stated that the Book of Revelations, 22:12, was allegorical, and directed the use of botanicals when it stated: "And the leaves of the tree of life were for the healing of the nations." Once in his youth he had stood before the gateway of the great medical school at Salerno, and read its motto: *Si Tibi deficiant medici, medici tibi fiant, haec tria, mens hilaris, requies, moderata dieta.* (If doctors fail to cure you, take these three doctors: a happy mind, recreation, and a moderate diet.)

This old G.P. was getting results without employing the technique of poisonous insects, poisonous vipers and a large portion of modern young doctors, steeped in the miasm of medical monopoly — that technique being the use of a hypodermic needle to introduce synthetic chemicals into the blood stream and pollute it with all sorts of unnatural garbage, far too often to the detriment of the patient. He knew that although some of these potions seemed temporarily to obtain some good, he also knew that that same patient, some time in the future, was going to have to pay the price in invalidism, fearful suffering and untimely death.

Dr. James Pressing had seen whole myriads of "wonder" and "miracle" drugs rise like a U.S. intercontinental missile and fizzle away every time the great drug houses had a new brain storm, far too often leaving incurable conditions. In fact, Dr. Pressing was a successful doctor, and as he bore no man's yoke, was vastly hated by organized medical greed as exemplified by nearly all of the so-called scientific medical societies. Dr. Pressing held (and he was right as has been proved very often indeed) that any type of medicine should be administered by mouth and go through digestion just as food is digested. He had seen very many serious abscesses left in patients because the attending doctor had not used a sterilized hypo needle.

And now, as our young friend, John Marsh is slowly but surely being returned to health, let us study the cause of the tragedy that had deprived him of both of his parents in one fell blow.

* * *

John's mother, whose maiden name was Della Smith, had been a wholesome, hearty, healthy girl until she had married John's father. The father, when it came to any knowledge of the love play between a man and his mate, in order to prepare her for connubial blisses, was as ignorant as a baboon and behaved like a bull in a china shop from the time he had married Della. Della, poor child, was equally ignorant and what she did know was conveyed to her in whispers by girls equally ignorant. On her entry into young womanhood, her criminally ignorant mother had not told her of that function possessed by women of that certain age. Della was simply horrified when she saw the menstrual flow coming from her body, and tried to clean up the matter by washing in cold water at the little brook. She caught cold and from that time on her periods were completely unpredictable.

After a whirlwind courtship, John's father married her, and as we have observed, behaved like the proverbial bull in a china shop. Della went through the tortures of the damned for three years, then John was born. It was a difficult birth — an instrumental delivery that tore her so badly that twenty-one stitches were required to sew her together again. It was bruited around, sub rosa, that the obstetrician did not know his art and had given her a monumental dose, by hypo, of course, of anterior pituitary gland extract, and that was the basis of all her future troubles. There is a time and a condition in which this medicine may be safely used – within due limits. But used unwisely it is a dope of the devil, but a magnificent piece of property to those making it.

Della's health continued to decline. She was conveyed to a clinic at St. Louis, and came home minus her ovaries; a piece of surgery now condemned in 85% of all cases by decent disciples of Hippocrates, the father of medicine. She rallied for a short time and then the decline re-commenced. This time she was taken to Chicago, to a very la-de-da medical monopoly hospital, the pride of the A.M.A. A hysterectomy was urged and later performed. After a long stay in the hospital and a longer period of convalescence in her home town, Della apparently picked up and began taking part in her usual church and other social activities. By this time her husband had taken to stepping out with the *demoiselles de joie,* and quondam friends of Della reported the truth and near-truths about the situation. Thereafter Della refused to share a bed with her husband.

Della was now having some mighty peculiar sensations in her abdomen and sought medical advice. A smart young surgeon tolled her again into surgery and a colostomy was performed. This piece of surgery was as little needed as removal of her head, because it was a psychosomatic condition brought about by her marital troubles, and her constant worry over the future of young John, who had declared he intended to become a physican like the beloved home physician, Dr. Pressing. Now, a colostomy is one of these operations that you should wish only on such men (?) as Adolph Hitler or Joe Stalin.

In simple words, the colon starts just above the appendix, rises to the hepatic flexure near the liver. It then turns across the abdomen as the transverse colon, another fairly sharp turn downward forms the descending colon.

The section of the colon arising from the appendix area is called the caecum, or ascending colon. (According to the attending medicine men, the operation performed on President Eisenhower dissected the last portion of the small intestine, called the ileum, at the ileo-caecal valve, and affixed it to the center of the transverse colon near the umbilicus, or navel. (May a medical graduate ask why?)

In the colostomy, a large opening is made in the colon usually near the hepatic flexure (just under the short ribs on the right side). This leaves all of the transverse colon, the descending colon, the sigmoid flexure, the rectum and the anus absolutely inactive. The bowel movements take place at the seat of surgery. The wound is not permitted to heal, and the constant fierce irritation and the mess of taking a daily enema in the wound drives most sufferers almost frantic. True, some lethargic patients can take this regime in its stride. Grin and bear it. But Della was not that kind of patient. She was as touchy and irritable as a hornet – and so the battle raged.

All this time, young John had secretly been visiting and talking to Dr. Pressing, and every talk made him more determined to become a doctor. In fact the good doctor was starting young John on the path to becoming the sort of physician that Hippocrates would have wished every doctor to be who took his Hippocratic Oath while crossing the fingers. Records prove the latter phrase. The day of the tragedy, John had been over to see Dr. Pressing and had served as assistant in a minor surgical operation – the excision and dressing of a fearful carbuncle. John did not flinch as he watched the lancet slice open the tissues and the blood and pus gush out. Most men would have fainted.

John had by this time gotten a pretty good idea that most of the surgery and suffering inflicted on his mother was for the benefit of the surgeon's pocket book. Dr. Pressing had just urged John to get a large scrap book and clip and paste important matter in the book, as well as to write his own ideas about things, medical and surgical. John washed up after the minor surgery and went home. As he entered the parlor and took up the book, his father and mother were at it again – or was it still at it? When he heard the blast of the revolver putting a bullet in his father's chest, and heard the heart-rending moan as he fell dead, he was thrown into a state of almost catalepsy. He was hardly conscious of the end of the tragedy when his mother shot herself to death. But he did remember, like a phantom of the past, her urgent call to take the money left him and become a real doctor with all the title, regardless of school, implies.

* * *

When John was able to get up and around, he found himself something of a hero. Not because he had done anything heroic, but because he had seen a terrific drama and come out with a $30,000 insurance bequest. Thirty thousand dollars was something to conjure with in those halcyon days. Naturally some of Della's and some of his dad's folks wanted to be appointed guardian and executor when the matter came up before the Probate Court. The judge happened to be one of those rare specimens who cared not a whit about re-election and called on John to express his preference as to his future. Without a moment's hesitation, John asked that his friend and medical mentor, Dr. Pressing, be appointed, and it was done on the spot.

Dr. Pressing had a wife who was worthy of him in every respect and seconded the motion that John come and live with them while he served the best way to begin medicine – a medical apprenticeship under a real, an honest, an unusually successful doctor. Dr. Pressing started John off on the right track by buying him a large scrap-note book and supervising his first entries. He told him to read the newspapers and magazines of all kinds, searching for anything – everything concerning medicine. And thus began the most enriching experience that may happen to any apprentice because:

Foul deeds will rise though all the world withhold them to men's eyes. – Shakespeare.

At the age of eighteen John finished high school *cum laude.* Dr. Pressing took him into the woods at every opportunity and taught him how to identify and use the various botannical components of St. John's Tree of Life. He showed John digitalis, hydrastis, catnip, echinacea, lady slipper, belladona, aconite, skullscap, and myriads more of God's kind of drugs that could outcure disease far quicker and better than abortions made from coal tar and oil wells for the enrichment of Germany and her war lords.

He pointed out and proved that the best remedies had been discovered and used by people who never saw the inside of a medical school. There was quinine, discovered by the ancient Peruvians and handed over to Spanish monks to become the one great treatment for malaria. (God had grown the cinchona tree for the healing of the nations at a location where it was most needed. Quinine comes from the cinchona tree). A weak and weary old lady in England discovered the value of digitalis in heart diseases. It is still the remedy *par excellence* after three centuries. Learned doctors sought to have her burned as a witch after they had appropriated her great discovery.

Dr. Pressing took down some wise old books written by some mighty wise doctors, who had stood and fought along with Aesculapius in curing patients other doctors, with their vile poisons, had failed to help. There was Dr. A. O'Leary of Jefferson Medical College, who had written: "The best things in the healing art have been done by those that never had a medical diploma – the first Caesarian section, the lithotomy, the use of cinchona (quinine), ether as an anesthetic, treatment of the air passages by inhalation (every doctor today who knows his medicine uses inhalation of medicated steam, instead of the sulpha drugs that have killed thousands, and chloromycetin, killer of more thousands with aplastic anemia), the water cure (hydrotherapy that good doctors prescribe for patients at Hot Springs and a hundred other spas), electricity, (what doctor does not use the sine wave, diathermy, short wave and other modalities such as X-rays, ultra violet and infra red, all produced by electricity), faith cure (as at Lourdes), mind cure (psychiatry, psychology, psychosomatics, neuro-psychology, etc.)

Dr. Pressing showed John the statement of Professor Benjamin Rush, of America's largest and probably best medical college in existence. Dr. Rush stated in words of crystal clarity: "Remember how many of our useful remedies have been discovered by quacks."

This reminds us of Harry Hoxsey, a humanitarian called quack by orthodox medicine, who has discovered a remedy that is *curing* all types of cancer. Yet the higher echelon members in the A.M.A. call him quack and charlatan. How do they dare to do it and then face a justly indignant Maker? The A.M.A. ordered its lobbyists and administrations in government to condemn Dr. Harry Hoxsey and his proved treatment for cancer. Senator Tobey's committee empowered Benedict FitzGerald, of the U.S. Department of Justice, to investigate and report. FitzGerald went over the country and investigated. He reported to Senator Tobey the most dastardly, malignant, jealous, selfish, rascally conduct of the leaders of the A.M.A. Senator Tobey died. The chairmanship was handed by the political scoundrels in our once free and decent government, to a man named Bricker.

Bricker thrust this report – the most important report to a congressional committee since the war of 1812 – into a pigeon hole (some declare Bricker had it destroyed) and refuses to this day even to meet with FitzGerald and discuss the stranglehold the A.M.A. and the F.D.A. has on the American people. The F.D.A. franked a large placard to every U.S. postoffice and there they hang, accusing Dr.

Harry Hoxsey, the man who has cured thousands of cases of cancer of all types, condemning a treatment that Washington never investigated. If the F.D.A. says it has investigated, it is the most damnable set of liars since Ananias.

The FitzGerald report states in plain words: "There is reason to believe that the A.M.A. has been hasty, capricious, arbitrary and outright dishonest . . . . the alleged machination of Dr. J. J. Moore (for the past ten years the treasurer of A.M.A.) could involve the A.M.A. and others in an interstate conspiracy of alarming proportions. Behind and over all this is the weirdest conglomeration of corrupt motives, intrigue, selfishness, jealousy, obstruction and conspiracy I have ever seen."

My good Americans, in the words of this honest and fearless man: "How long will the American people take this?" How long *will* we take it? Hoxsey is curing cancer. Twenty thousand residents of Ohio die from cancer every year, proving that surgery, radium and X-rays are almost a complete failure. Will the good people of Ohio return Bricker to the U.S. Senate again? If they do, then they richly deserve the torments of cancer here, and most certainly some form of condign punishment hereafter.

And what shall be the fate of the scoundrels who malignantly and feloniously placed their hands on the Word of Almighty God and swore, in His ineffable name, to protect the folks who pay them ten times what their services, if any, are worth? We can only call to mind the words of the judge when he has sentenced a criminal to death: "May God have mercy on your soul."

It is positively known that the use of tobacco causes tens of thousands of cases of cancer, hundreds of thousands of cases of heart disease, hypertension that will kill 32,000,000 Americans, cerebral paralysis, Buerger's disease, where the flesh rots and falls from the bones. *That is known and admitted.* Why doesn't the A.M.A. and the authorities in Washington put out placards warning against tobacco? Is the tobacco trust stronger than the United States?

* * *

When young John Marsh was about 18, he graduated from High School. He led the class. After the graduation exercises, Dr. Pressing called him into his private office and entered into a conversation that was to make John Marsh Pressing one of the greatest physicians the world has known plus the greatest of crusaders against monopoly in medicine and rascality in government. After chatting for a few minutes, Dr. Pressing asked: "John, do you still want to become a physician?" The reply being definitely affirmative, Dr. Pressing continued: "You have the making of a great doctor, for you have a heart for suffering people; you are definitely not an atheist. I think one of the main causes of brutality and heartlessness exhibited by a large cross section of doctors is because they are atheists.

"Believe me the old Latin was right when he said:

Ubi tres medici Ibi duo Athei.

(The writer would like to add to the atheist charge a still more damnable activity engaged in by far too many medical students – I refer to the vivisection of man's best friends, dogs and cats. The Nuremburg trial proved that the S.S. devil doctors first did vivisection of animals under anesthesia. They graduated to animal experiments without pain-relieving drugs. Becoming ennuied with that as "kid stuff," they next went into vivisection of human beings under anesthesia. Finally they reached the dregs of degradation by torturing thousands upon thousands of human beings without anesthesia.

Dr. Thedford Taylor, who was active in the trial of those beastly German doctors, pointed out that despite all this human slaughter and satanic sadism, medicine had not profited an iota. If nothing was gained by human vivisection, what possible good can we expect by torturous deaths of our lesser brothers, because of the dissimilarity of the species, physically and spiritually? We must give dogs a spiritual preference over the Nazi beasts.)

Dr. Pressing went on: "John, Mother and I never had any children, and we have come to love you as if you were our own son. We have talked it over many times and want you to do us the great honor to adopt you as our son. Mother and I are getting up in years, and we would esteem it a great blessing if you would become our son. Please say yes."

John's eyes were awash as he replied: "I could think of no greater blessing here or hereafter than to be your son. I never knew any real happiness until I came to live with you, Dad. Let us take Mother and get it settled."

In two weeks the three appeared before the probate court and John Marsh became, in the eyes of God and of man, John Marsh Pressing.

As it happened there was a good medical preparatory college about twenty miles away and preparations were pushed to launch John Marsh Pressing's pre-medical course. As there was very good train service, John was able to be at home nearly every evening and return by an early train each morning. His new Dad, Dr. Pressing, started his real career by looking up an old, old copy of the divine Oath of Hippocrates and coaching his new son in learning it until it was to appear before his mind's eye whenever any perplexing problem might face him in his future career as a physician. There was a time when this Oath was entered into proudly by every graduate in medicine. But, surprising as it may seem, and shocking too, it has been little more than a scrap of paper since George H. Simmons took over the A.M.A. lock, stock and barrel and turned it into just what Benedict FitzGerald reported it: a dishonorable, dishonest racket.

Simmons had run an advertised, quack, charlatan den of iniquity called a hospital or clinic, of which he was the chief-thief. The business was mostly criminal abortions plus a cancer quackery that would have shamed the very devil. Nevertheless, he took over the A.M.A. in its entirety. A.M.A. medicine cannot cure cancer today. How was the great Simmons formula lost if it ever existed — which it definitely did not? But Simmons did not criminally oppose anything that might have promise of curing cancer as the modern A.M.A. does. What can be said of the present official setup of the A.M.A. that deliberately lies and tries to prevent known cancer cures to be employed without persecution? Why didn't A.M.A. doctors save the lives of Senator Taft, Senator Vandenberg, Babe Zaharias and millions of other cancer patients if Simmons knew how?

In view of this, how many cases that A.M.A. doctors point out as cured by surgery, radium and X-rays, may possibly have been mis-diagnosed and declared cured when no cancer existed? Or how many were straight-out cases of racketeering? Read my documented record herein and judge justly.

During his two years in pre-med, John had little time for society because he knew the fearful grind that was before him, and Dr. Pressing had thoroughly impressed on him the unquestionable necessity of learning each lesson thoroughly before going to the next one. Thus no problem was insurmountable. He told John the ancient Greek fable of a task that seemed impossible at first glance. It was decreed by the Parcae that the man to earn a certain great honor must carry a full-size, full-grown bull on his shoulders and place it at the sacrificial table. A certain middle age man decided that his son was to have the honor, so he bought a young calf and had the boy shoulder it and carry it around. As the young bull grew and developed in size, the boy's strength grew at a parallel rate. When the boy had reached his majority, he easily shouldered the full-grown bull and carried it to the sacred spot.

"That is the way to learn," remarked Dr. Pressing. "Do each stint right today and tomorrow's task is easily done."

Through those two preparatory years, John attended patients with his Dad and, even before entering into his four-year medical course, he was a skilled diagnostician, anesthetist, and had an extraordinary knowledge of *materia medica.* And most important he had learned that the natural condition of the human body is health. And that every individual has what is called *vis naturae medicatrix,* that divine attribute, or gift, that makes man self-healing in a large proportion of cases if not interfered with by any modern hocus pocus with synthetic coal tar chemicals and hypodermic pollution of the blood stream.

One day, shortly before he took off for pre-medical college at a large city some 250 miles from his home town, John asked his Dad to make a full explanation of the Oath of Hippocrates. This is the too-often broken unbreakable oath that too many graduates take with many mental reservations, if one will only keep his eyes open and observe. The most damnable thing about it all is that the A.M.A. and its branches has full punitive powers but apparently wears blinders and does not see the vicious practices some of its members commit. The record is full of cases of over-charging, un-needed surgery, ghost surgery, kick-backs and downright rascality. And in vicious cases of malpractice, the medical societies form a dense protective wall of the most contumaceous order.

Dr. Pressing took down his framed Oath of Hippocrates and he and his young protege repeated it together. Here is the modified modern version, which should be far stronger than it is.

THE OATH OF HIPPOCRATES

You do most solemnly swear, each by what we hold most sacred, that you will be loyal to the profession of medicine and just and generous to its members; that you will lead your lives and practice your art in uprightness and honor; that into whatsoever house you shall enter, it shall be for the good of the sick to the utmost of your power, you holding yourself aloof from wrong, from corruption, from the tempting of others to vice; that you will exercise your art solely for the cure of your patients and will give no drug, perform no operation for a criminal purpose, even if solicited, far less suggest it; that whatsoever you shall see or hear of the lives of men, which is not fit to be spoken, you will keep inviolably secret. These things do you swear. Let each man bow his head in sign of acquiescence. And now, if you will be true to this, your oath, may prosperity and good repute be ever yours; the opposite if you shall prove yourselves foresworn.

"You see, my boy, the Oath has been much abbreviated and some of the most protective portions eliminated or watered down so that some of the rascals in the practice of medicine – and thank God, a large share of the doctors are honest and honorable – may commit the most dastardly crimes against those who have placed their trust in the doctor. But it still remains powerful, if doctors live up to it. Or if the medical monopoly societies cease playing politics, and punish those who break their oath."

"That seems pretty hard to believe," remarked John. "May I have a little proof, although I know you would not make such an awful charge without proof."

Dr. Pressing replied: "Now, son, that shows you why you should keep right after that diary scrap book." He got up and withdrew a large scrap book from among what seemed to be a multitude of like scrap books, flipped over the pages until he came to a certain section, and handed the book to John to read. "Just suppose you read that and brief it out loud," remarked the doctor.

John read and briefed a few from possibly millions of such cases of rascality in men who had supposedly take that unbreakable Holy Oath of Hippocrates.

"Well," he said, "from what I see here, so many doctors in New York City were accused of rascality and racketeering that Governor Thomas Dewey appointed the Morland Committee to investigate and report. My good grief, it's unbelievable. Thousands of New York doctors were proved guilty of ghost surgery, demanding and receiving kickbacks, unnecessary surgery at fabulous, ruining fees. They demanded and took bribes from surgeons, pharmacies, pharmaceutical and serum laboratories, opticians, optical goods houses. In fact," said the young fellow, "it seems they broke the sacred Oath into more pieces than Humpty Dumpty. But, Sir, was nothing done to correct this fetid situation? Were they not kicked out of the medical societies? If not, why? Didn't the State of New York prosecute them and sentence them to long prison terms?"

"My boy, you have yet to learn much about politics in the State and in the A.M.A. Some of the vilest polecats who ever graduated in medicine have been called before the bar of justice for heinous crimes and malpractice. But there is a rotten thing called 'medical ethics' and their colleagues, no matter how much they wished to be just and honest, feared repercussions from the medical societies. It is almost impossible to get a verdict, either in criminal or civil damage suits, against a member of the A.M.A. Many doctors have been caught in perjured testimony in an attempt to shield others of their kind, and the case hushed up. Not long since, some top brass surgeons, all members of A.M.A., operated on a man's abdomen and sewed him up. In a few days the unfortunate patient was taken with terrific pain. His belly was again opened up to find a 5-inch-long pair of steel forceps gouging his intestines."

"But, good heavens, what has been done about this crime?" asked John.

Doctor Pressing replied: "The matter has been hushed so thoroughly that one might well wonder if Peter at the Gate has the least record. I have known of many cases like this, some far worse."

John was about to ask some rather pointed questions, but at the moment he opened his mouth, the phone rang. Dr. Pressing was summoned to a long drive in the country to parry the scythe of the Death Angel, Azrael, with a dull curette and anything else that mortal medicine might have to offer.

CHAPTER 2

I will never provide an ecbolic bolus. – Hippocratic Oath.

Folks around the territory served by Dr. Pressing had by this time pretty well accepted John Marsh Pressing as a physician to be, and permitted him to enter the sick chamber with Dr. Pressing. This call was far beyond the Doctor's usual territorial line, which like the equator was imaginary, but there just the same. It seemed evident that Dr. Pressing had a premonition of what he was about to tackle because he carefully selected specula, an Elliott bag and other remedial agents he thought he might need.

As they drove out the newly-paved river road, the two men dropped into the subject always uppermost in the minds of every member of the healing art – regardless of the school, method, creed or clique (for one will always find cliques and gangs in any human operated organization). John was doing the driving and, as the car ate up the miles, he glanced at Dr. Pressing and asked: "What kind of a case are we going to find?"

"From the little I got from the patient, I am afraid we are going to find one of those nasty cases of puerperal sepsis, brought about by an attempted abortion. I just happened to hear that the girl had gotten into trouble; and she just got back from Chicago and had to be carried from the train."

"Funny I never heard about it," remarked John. "You surely get about."

"That's right, son, and let this be a good lesson to you. A doctor has to keep his ears to the ground, and his eyes wide open every minute of the day. And under his Oath he has to keep his mouth tight closed. I think you are going to see one of medicine's most valuable modalities in use – the Elliott bag. It far surpasses a whole drove of these new-fangled gadgets that clutter up every doctor's life, and are mainly of value to the manufacturer. I do hope that the foetus has passed and I do not crave to do a curettage at any time, especially with the putrid remains of an unborn dead child. But if so be, we will do the curretage, otherwise we are likely to find a defunct patient in a few days."

"Why didn't the folks call a doctor in whose territory the patient lives?" asked John.

"They did try to get doctors from all around them without success. Some doctors were really out on urgent calls. Others were just too disinterested to make the call. And as there really is an acute shortage of doctors, despite the mendacities of the medical big-wigs, these folks had to shop around until they found a doctor who would make the call. I believe that many doctors – thousands of them – do not make the call because the poor sufferers are suspected of being unable to pay the fancy fees now with us."

"Dad, I want to ask you a question, and I trust you to give me the answer right from the shoulder. The other day an M.D. handed me a pamphlet from the medical society that really tore into all forms of drugless healing. Their rancor seems to have been mainly directed toward this new art of healing called Chiropractic. But they also lit into about everything and everybody except orthodox Allopathic medicine. I would dearly love to have your observations on the healers who do not strictly adhere to the layout of the A.M.A."

Dr. Pressing looked meditatively for a few minutes across a large field of golden wheat that was full ripe for the reapers. He slowly and carefully set forth the opinion of every honest man. "Son, when Jesus of Nazareth was on earth in the form of a human being, he went about healing all manner of diseases without any form of medicine whatsoever. And he never solicited or accepted remuneration. The learned doctors of medicine and of the Jewish Church accused him of healing by calling in Beelzebub, the god of flies, or dung, to do the healing. The thing that hurt the so-called doctors was that Jesus healed, not by himself, but by being able to direct the healing power of God. He used no drugs. And He said: "These things and more shall ye do."

John interrupted to ask: "But what proof have we that there was any such person as Jesus? And what proof have we that He cured people – or rather, that healing came through Him to sick people?"

"We have absolute proof that He lived and healed," said Dr. Pressing. The Jewish Talmud was written by Jews, for Jews and to Jews; I mean orthodox Jews who hated Jesus worse than the devil allegedly hates holy water. The Talmud was written from about 200 B.C. to about 400 A.D. It is still in existence for anyone to read. Rawlinson made a fine translation of it. The Talmud speaks with the utmost hatred and abhorrence of Jesus, but, at the same time admitted that Jesus of Nazareth healed the incurable on the spot. How dare anybody deny what Jesus' most hating enemies admit?

"No. my son, Jesus Christ really lived and anybody that doubts it, if he will look up the records, is either a confounded liar, or a consummate idiot. After all, medical doctors do not heal, or cure. Nature heals, the doctor collects, according to wise, old Benjamin Franklin. Have you that miserable, lying pamphlet on you?"

John, while never taking his eyes from the road, slipped this piece of A.M.A. fiction out of his hip pocket and handed it to his new Dad.

Dr. Pressing took it and scanned the contents. "The usual scramble of A.M.A. rot," he snapped, "written by a man who doesn't know his rear elevation from a post hole. No doubt some of the top scarecrows in organized banditry in medicine wrote it. Today several million honest folks accept healing treatments from drugless practitioners. That number of people just cannot all be wrong. This conglomeration of mendacities points out a few cases in which patients received Chiropratic treatments and died. That may, or may not be true. But how many cases have been killed by medical harpies?

"Son, get me right, I am for any system of healing that will cure the most patients, and I do not care what it is called. Here in this piece, the A.M.A. author reports probably false records that he hopes will redound to the glory of the medical monopoly. But he carefully refrains to look for the cases healed by, or through Chiropractic, Naprapathy, Christian Science, and Unity. And he carefully avoids reporting that countless such healings have been made after orthodox Allopathy has dismally failed."

"But, Dad, if all this is true, why should I spend years in preparation for medical practice?"

The doctor replied: "Because any form of treatment that heals is honorable and laudable and Almighty God smiles on it. I want you to have the best medical education that can be provided. But if you are as awake as I feel you are to the misery that surrounds us on every side, and which medicine alone has failed, you will also study Osteopathy, Chiropractic, Faith Healing, Unity and Christian Healing. Then employ any or all of them for the glory of God and the good of your patients."

"Dad, your word is good enough for me. Is there such a thing as Spiritual and Faith Healing?"

"Absolutely! Hippocrates, whole centuries before Christ, stated that proved theorem. And let me tell you that when the A.M.A. makes sport of Chiropractic and laughs at the Palmers because, as the A.M.A. claims, D.D. Palmer was a fish peddler — *I call on every Christian on earth to witness that Jesus Christ chose most of His disciples from the fishers and told them He would make them fishers of men.* I furthermore declare to you that there are, in Britain, men called spiritual or psychic healers, who very often heal the most obdurate diseases after orthodox medicine has miserably failed.

"I have seen decent, honorable practitioners of regular medicine and surgery cure diseases after all other forms have failed. Believe me, John, no system has it all, by a hundred million light years. Furthermore, I can name a dozen of the most reputable medical doctors on earth who come right out and tell the truth – that prayer and faith cure. Well, our destination is that house over there by the old-time water power mill. I fear we have a real piece of work cut out for us. But firm in what knowledge we have, and ably assisted by two great healing remedies that modern advocates of medical greed have rejected, we will do our very best and leave the results to God power – the *vis naturae medicatrix.*

"John, an old time country doctor, a man such as Hippocrates would have wished every doctor to be, Dr. Arthus E. Hertzler, wrote the most marvelous book that exists on earth, especially for the young doctor who wants to be a real physician. It is called *Horse And Buggy Doctor.* We are going to read that together at every opportunity. It is the most factual and at the same time most interesting book I have ever read. The trouble with so many modern doctors is that they either do not believe in a God of Love, or else they have made Him a mere back seat driver. Dr. Hertzler once said, or quoted some other grand physician: 'A man who denies there is a God, is a fool.' Yes, son, we must really make a thorough study of Hertzler's grand book. Well, here we are and somehow or other I dread it."

John brought the Ford to a stop and the two stepped out, bag in hand and mounted the steps of a very pretty bungalow cottage. A woman of perhaps 50 years came to meet them and explain why the very long trip. They had called seven doctors. For some unaccountable reason four of them refused to come. Three doctors really were at work on His business.

Dr. Pressing said: "Before seeing the sick girl I wish to ask you a few questions, because I suppose the patient is in no shape to answer coherently. First: is the patient married?" The reply being in the negative, he next asked: "Was an illegal operation performed on her when she went to Chicago?"

The mother replied: "All I know is that she took to skylarking around with the choir leader of the church, and the next thing I knew she told me her periods had stopped. She admitted intimacy with the rascal. He refused to marry her so she went to Chicago to have the mess cleared up."

"Did she pass the foetus, the unborn child?"

"No," said the woman.

"We will see her now," said Dr. Pressing. "Please lead the way."

The mother conducted them down a long hall and entered a door at the very end. The odor arising when the two men entered the room was almost overwhelming. On the bed, a young woman who could not have been over 25 years old, lay gasping for every breath. Her complexion was that of a corpse before the mortician treats the face and adds rouge and lipstick. Dr. Pressing pulled down the covers and took a look at an abdomen that was swelled to almost double the normal size. Her pulse was thin and thready and her heart was missing beats. She was burning with a fever of 103°. The case seemed extremely critical and Dr. Pressing held some doubt whether the patient could be saved. There was but one thing to do and that was to get the decaying foetal remains out and attempt to set the field for recovery by curetting the inner layer of the uterus and then use the Elliott bag for intense hyperemia. Hyperemia means a largely increased supply of fresh blood in an area, which would bring oxygen and carry away the toxic metabolic products.

Here was a case like that recorded by Hertzler in his *Horse And Buggy Doctor.* A case that must be handled in a country home, without any of the fantastic gadgets so many modern doctors demand in treating even a small pimple.

The girl was raised and a rubber sheet placed under her. She was then turned in bed until her hips rested at the very edge and her heels held to the bed rails. She was only semiconscious, somewhat delirious and too sick to raise any protest. As in many country homes there were several old-style kitchen lamps provided with a metallic reflector. A bivalve speculum was then inserted and spread wide.

For some reason only known to God, the manipulation described brought on labor pains and in a few minutes the three-month foetus began emerging from the uterus so rapidly that Dr. Pressing took out the speculum to give the right of way to the unborn remains of the child. In the meantime, John was in the kitchen boiling much water and sterilizing a dull curette. Within half an hour the foetus was out of the way, and Dr. Pressing lightly scraped the wall of the womb with the curette and brought away the placenta, or afterbirth. He then sprayed the inside with a new form of soluble iodine that had but recently come from Germany and was reported to have given excellent results in just such cases. The drug was entirely unlike ordinary tincture of iodine, was non-toxic, and could be used intravenously when carefully supervised by a competent doctor. The girl, who had apparently been in jeopardy of her life, now showed a change for the better. John came in bringing the Elliott outfit and gallons of hot water at about 108°. Although the Elliott bag is one of the greatest curative agents ever devised, most unfortunately far too many medical doctors have not even learned to use it, preferring, if they do know, to use the modern drugs of destruction, designed to make large incomes for the German dye cartels and their American stooges of the pharmaceutical houses. Not to mention the fact that the "miracle", "wonder" or "blunder" drugs are like King David, killing their tens of thousands, and making once decent doctors into mere assistants to the assistants of the drug cartels. Who has forgotten the disasters that followed the use of the sulpha drugs, the mass killings from chloromycetin, the fearful reactions and side chains from all or nearly all of the products of the barnyard and the slaughtering abatoirs? These statements are only too true. It is also too true that every doctor who has practiced medicine over a third century has seen them come, make millions for unconscionable commercialism, so that the great Dr. C. A. Stephens wrote:

"If Demand calls for things that will kill countless orphans a great distance away, Supply will furnish them, and collect its dirty, blood-stained pence. That, they say, is, good business."

Simply stated, the Elliott bag is a soft rubber bag that is thrust into the vagina or anus. It has two tubes – one to admit hot water, and the other to carry it away. At times, according to the indications, cold water may be prescribed instead of hot water. This apparatus has obtained results that other gadgets whose benefits are largely to the manufacturers, will never equal. And it is absolutely safe, even when used by a layman.

In an hour the normal *vis naturae medicatrix*, or the God-given natural healing power of the patient, took over and her temperature dropped to 101.5°. In addition she could now speak quite coherently and rationally.

Dr. Pressing collected some of the corruption accompanying the foetus and placed it in a large-mouth bottle to take back home, for he intended to prepare the really marvelous Dr. Duncan remedy that was to be used by mouth, instead of shooting pollution into a blood stream already over-loaded with filth. As any doctor, who knows the ABCs of medicine, and has a conscience, understands the reports of disasters following penicillin, aureomycin, chloromycetin, sulpha and the dozens of other new, "scientific remedies" it was most fortunate that Dr. Duncan made one of the most important discoveries known in medicine. In all sorts of staph and strep infections it is the remedy *par excellence* because it cures without side reactions, whereas practically all of the modern antibiotics are not safe, can never be made safe when introduced via the technique of venomous serpents, disease-bearing insects like the mosquito, the tsetse fly, the louse, the bed bug and the flea – that is, by injection into a living body.

What a crime it is that medical instructors do not learn of the actually miraculous results from the Elliott bag, the

Duncan technique, and the jury mast. And having learned them, it is a still greater crime that they do not convey the knowledge to the medical students. May this be the reason: No honest doctor denies that there is an acute shortage of physicians. Doctor's offices and hospitals are always running over. Therefore the average medical doctor will not take the proper amount of time to make a careful examination, without the use of insensible gadgets, then supply a proper diagnosis and treatment – in nearly all cases by mouth, or other open orifice. No so-called "wonder" drug can supply the needs of the ailing human body. And snap diagnoses are likely to be as inept and crude as cases of love at first sight between a Russian marine and some young prostitute wandering the streets in search of prey.

During the next two hours the patient noticeably improved, Dr. Pressing took John off to one side and said: "I want you to stay here and keep that Elliott bag working straight through at a temperature of not less than 106°. I will go home, prepare the Duncan solution, nap for a single hour, and be back here in not over four hours. Give her one of these tablets every two hours. It looks like we have just saved a life. Do not permit her to talk too much to you as she must save her strength. But listen to what she says and it is possible we will get the name of the murderer who committed this crime. Here, take my ℞ book and jot down anything she says that appears important."

Young John followed him out to the car. "Dad," he declared vehemently, "I once read that Kung-Fu-Sze wrote: 'One seeing is better than ten thousand words.' For the first time I get his wisdom. I'm the luckiest young fellow on earth. This day I have learned something I could not get in a six-year medical course – and for free."

* * * * *

In three hours 55 minutes Dr. Pressing arrived at the patient's home with Dr. Duncan's solution that has saved thousands of lives from the brink of the future life. He found that those four hours had done much for the sufferer. Her natural color was returning, her heart action was almost normal and her temperature was now down to 100°. This girl was going to make it.

After a careful and complete examination, Dr. Pressing left directions for the use of the Duncan treatment, and asked that he be contacted by telephone every day for a week. He also wrote out a schedule of diet of the right kind of foods because already commercialism had begun to debauch and destroy humanity by the addition of chemicals as foreign to food as an angel of light differs from Satan or a doctor who perjures himself by breaking his sacred Oath of Hippocrates.

On their way home the two, father and adopted son, entered into a discussion that was to conduct the future John Marsh Pressing through the pitfalls and evils of twentieth century medical mendacity to become one of the best general practitioners in America. How strange it is that recently certain big-wigs of the medical and mechanical association have announced with a fanfare of trumpets and the roll of drums that far too many doctors sought to be specialists, whereas what was needed was more general practitioners — the doctor who hears your first baby shriek at your first spanking, and the last moan you utter as your spiritual body leaves its house of clay.

After driving along for some ten minutes, John said: "Dad, will that woman fully recover her health?"

"It's hard to say because I examined some of the sequelae of the abortion and found a fearful conglomeration of bacteria, including the Neisser bacillus, which, as you already know, is the etiological factor in 'clap' or gonorrhea. If the gonococcus gets up into her tubes and possibly to the ovaries, she may develop Neisserian rheumatism. It may be necessary to clean house by removing practically all of her generative organs and leave her a hollow shell, or husk of a woman. If anything will prevent that it will be derived from that Duncan solution. By the way, did she mention the polecat who performed that slaughterhouse job of abortion?"

"Yes, she did," replied John. "I have it in my notes."

"I will bet my shirt that he is a leader in medical politics. We will look up his name in the medical directory when we get home and I intend to write direct to the president of the A.M.A. I know this will do no good, but it will give me just one more opportunity to blow off steam."

They drove along in silence for a time, each busy with his own thoughts. Finally Dr. Pressing said: "Son, I am not a prophet, but let me make a prediction you will find will come true. There is evidently a conspiracy between some medical leaders and some serum and vaccine manufacturers. Already one with eyes can see the tendency. You will live to see the day when the serum plants will bring out vaccines of every kind for every disease. They will make millions. Then along will come another crop of diseases to displace those just conquered. The newspaper writers will rant and rave and I will even tell you what they will call these new concoctions. They will call them 'miracle' drugs and people will take them even though perfectly healthy.

Thus the once holy art of medicine will be a racket of the vilest order. For instance, I have seen diphtheria antitoxin save lives and seen it take lives. Bezredka, the authority on serology, pointed out the after effects of inoculation and it was named the Bazredka reaction. Remember, John, when these conditions arise, that I told you in advance. I also declare, on my honor, that it is my most positive conviction that these foreign bodies shot into the very life blood of ignorantly innocent victims will sooner or later bring forth an enormously increased incidence of cancer, hypertension, kidney diseases, heart diseases, and Reynaud's disease."

(Author's note: This prediction made by an honorable and reputable physician, a graduate from Washington University medical school, has come true to the very finest detail. Dr. John Marsh Pressing will discover this after he has gone into practice. And he will give the documented evidence in detail.)

"But, Dr. Pressing, if medicine is going to be such a rotten mess, why should I take years out of my life to become a doctor? Why not start a pharmacy with the money I have from my parents?"

Dr. Pressing answered: "Because medicine, worthily and honestly practiced – and that goes for all honest means of preventing and healing diseases – is a holy thing. It is getting fearfully putrid since Simmons took the A.M.A. over. It must be saved and brought back to its pristine state of working right alongside God. The medical worms have eaten their way to the middle just as another and less dangerous set of worms eat their way from the surface to the core of an apple.

"When mother cooks apples for us, she opens the apple and carefully cuts away the spoiled portion with the worms. It must be so with the situation that now grows worse every year in the treatment of the sick. Good young doctors, like you, must open the wormy apple, dissect the rot and the worms. The good portion will then be used for human, healthy living. Perhaps this is not a perfect metaphor, but you certainly grasp my meaning. With the knowledge you are gaining every day as you go around with me, you should become one of the greatest physicians alive. You can go into medical society meetings and tell off the bastardisers of our art – and you will get away with it."

"Well," replied John Marsh Pressing, "I will surely do my level best to carry out your ideas. Speaking of the doctor that brought about an abortion in the patient we have just visited, makes me think of Dr. C........ who lives right in our midst. He is a pillar in the medical society, off-shoot of the parent A.M.A. at Chicago. I personally know that he tells the young sprouts around our section to go ahead with their sex affairs, and if they get the girls pregnant he will do an abortion for $25.00. I also know that three girls in Glasgow have died trom puerperal sepsis. That is the right name for child-bed fever, isn't it?"

"Right you are," replied Dr. Pressing. "Do not think, my boy, that I do not know of this and worse. He used a hypo syringe on a syphlitic patient and, without sterilizing the needle, he used it on a young girl. I am now treating her for that disease. From some symptoms I am fearful that the spirochete has attacked her nervous system. Boy, cerebral syphilis is a fearful thing. Never forget this: there are times when hypodermic medication is indicated. Dipping the needle in alcohol is not enough. If you do not have an extra, clean needle with you, be sure and flame the one you must use. Use a match if nothing else is at hand."

"I'll never forget strict asepsis, believe me," replied the future Dr. John Marsh Pressing. After a few moments of thought, he continued: "Dad, what is the sense in taking two-year pre-medic? And who instituted such an asinine idea? Does a knowledge of anti-diluvian history, or Sanskrit verbal conjugations assist the doctor in doing what we did today?"

"Son, the greatest doctors who ever lived did not have any pre-medical course except what you are getting from day to day. Proponents of this idiocy say it gives the doctor-to-be culture, makes him a gentleman. What the suffering patient wants is relief from pain, and healing, not gobs of more or less quasi-medical mumbo-jumbo. Millions of patients are mal-diagnosed and mal-treated while a group of medical stooges sit around and throw the gentleman cow." He slipped his hand into his coat pocket and brought forth a small memorandum book. "Slow up a bit, son, I want to read you some medical aphorisms, made by really good doctors, who cared not at all about much of this twaddle about science and scientific medicine.

"Here is what Professor Martin Paine of the N.Y. University Medical School said in his *Institutes of Medicine:* 'Remedial agents are essentially morbific (author: disease producing) in their operation. In curing one disease we produce another.' Now, son, here is another good one by Professor A. Clark, M.D. of the N.Y. College of Physicians and

Surgeons. He wrote: 'All of our curative agents are poisons, and as a consequence, every dose diminishes the patient's vitality.' Dr. J. M. Smith, of the same school, stated the same fact in slightly different words. Professor St. John, M.D. said: 'All medicines are poisonous.' Professor H. G. Cox M.D. said: 'The fewer remedies you employ in disease, the better for your patients.' Professor E. S. Carr, of the same school wrote: 'All drugs are more or less adulterated. The physician seldom knows how much of any drug he is administering.'

"Professor J. M. Smith, M.D. lectured: 'Drugs do not cure diseases; disease is cured by the *vis naturae medicatrix.'* (Author: the natural healing power of nature – that is, God). In fact, my boy, Professor Clark, M.D. stated right out: 'Physicians have hurried thousands to their graves who would have recovered if left to Nature.' But here comes the crusher for all this quasi-science jargon of the leaders in medical societies. Professor Gregory, M.D. of Edinburgh, Scotland, wrote: *'Gentlemen, ninety-nine out of every hundred medical facts are medical lies, and medical doctrines are, for the most part, stark, staring nonsense.'* Now, son, these things are not meant to scarce you away from God's noblest art – the art of preventing and healing diseases. And I care not what the system of healing, whether drugless, manipulative, faith, spiritual, or by the extremely careful use of the botanical drugs that were provided by a benevolent God for the healing of the nations.

"The curse of medicine today is the damnable dye makers who are producing new hell's kitchen brews so fast from coal tar – and coal tar is a prime suspect in cancer – *that they are now inventing new diseases on which to use their synthetic garbage.* If something is not done to curb these new compounds, such as aspirin, phenacetin, acetanilid and the like, cancer will be the universal disease. The true physician takes time to study the family history, he studies the sanitation and sanitary conditions in the residence, and then his best attention should be given to preventing diseases.

He must even go into the matter of food. No person can be healthy on a diet of white corn, sow belly and coffee. The true doctor knows the botanical plants indigenous to his territory and does not hesitate to use them when required. And he gets real results.

"Digitalis, a great heart remedy, was discovered by an old crone. None of this synthetic concoction can come within a mile of it. She collected and prepared the foxglove leaves and the so-called scientific doctors beat a path to her door. Well, here we are back home. This very day you have learned by seeing and doing things you will never get in any medical college, except in theory. Let's get mother to cook us up something and we will then go to the office."

CHAPTER 3

MEDICAL DIPLOMAS FOR SALE – CHEAP!

As Dr. Pressing and his protege' turned into the public square, they saw Dr. Jasper Callous get into his rattletrap auto and drive madly out of town. "I wonder what he is up to this time," observed Dr. Pressing. "No good, I'll be bound. That party has gotten away with murder so long and so often that it is a wonder some victim's relatives have not given him a hypo with a Colt revolver. I would bet my head that some victim has been put in the same shape as the one we just saw. And Callous is called on to correct his crime of abortion, or possibly sign a death certificate."

Young John asked: "How does he get away with it? Surely the medical society, a branch of the A.M.A., has punitive powers in such matters."

"There we find the reason why young men of character and intestinal fortitude should get into medicine and clean it out just as Hercules, in Greek mythology, cleaned out the accumulated manure from the Aegean stables. You see, my boy, Callous is the product of medical monopoly and chicanery in the State of Missouri. And I have no doubt this same thing exists in every state in the Union. What can one expect when he knows that one of the chain of A.M.A. controlled state medical journals stated: 'It is better to see a patient die under Allopathy than to see his life saved by Homeopathy.'

"Well, here we are at the office and the first thing to do is to look in my medical directory to see who and what the party is who performed that criminal operation on the patient we just left." Dr. Pressing flipped over the pages of a large book he picked up and in a few minutes found what he suspected. "Well," said he, "Here it is in the A.M.A. record. The guilty man is listed as a gynecologist. I note also that he is an officer in the local medical society, a scion of the A.M.A. Now, observe this." He picked up a large scrap book and showed John records that the gynecologist had been indicted and tried for abortions and resulting deaths. And yet, somehow or other, the cases against him had always been dropped. (Did the A.M.A. have anything to do with this? Why didn't that organization exert its undoubted punitive power? Why doesn't it right today exert that same punitive power against known doctors who demand and receive kick-backs from practically every organization that has anything to do with organized medicine? Or those who commit the crimes of urging unneeded surgery? Or those who take split fees, uncounted number of which doctors are known to the officialdom in organized medical greed? – Author)

Dr. Pressing then handed John a photostat of the rotten record of organized medical shysters in Missouri. The damning record read: "When the Carnegie Foundation for the Advancement of Teaching set out to regulate and rule education in the United States, the A.M.A. decided to join in it to regulate and eliminate certain medical schools." (Author's note: Is this the same group that has often been charged with conspiracy to force the Union into all sorts of international intrigue? The Press has had much to say that seemed highly culpable. I would not make any such charge. However, the similarity in names seems just a bit more than highly suspicious. And suddenly the so-called Free Press stopped recording these activities. One might, with considerable hope of the advancement of knowledge, look up and consider the source of the Carnegie millions. There is, for instance, the matter of the fraudulent and defective armor plate furnished at skyhigh prices furnished to the U.S. Navy.) The photostatic record continued: "The Homeopathic and Eclectic colleges were first on the list for elimination. In 1906 there were four of them in Missouri and they conformed in every respect to the laws governing medical instruction in that state.

"The State Board of Health was composed of seven members: five A.M.A. type Allopaths, one Homeopath and one

Eclectic. (Author's note: A bit of information is in order. The Eclectic system teaches that there is good in all systems, and that the physician should accept that which is best from all, discarding that which is not for the best good to the patients.) Their appointment and acts are dictated from North Dearborn Street, Chicago, (The American Medical Association, that is). The Board was not salaried, but got their per diem and expenses. That not being enough for neophyte medical politicians, the following scheme was cooked up: The five Allopaths refused to accept the Homeo and Eclectic medical schools as 'reputable', according to the Carnegie dictum, so many first class medical graduates went into court and forced the Board to issue them licenses. Many refused to sue, but just went ahead and practiced anyway. This, according to one fine physician, led to the medical shakedown that has persisted in Missouri for over sixteen years.

"Licenses to practice medicine were sold like groceries over the counter and for cash on the barrelhead. A No. 1 A.M.A. man, Dr. Adcox, of St. Louis was employed by the Board, which as stated, was composed of five A.M.A. doctors, a Homeopath and an Eclectic, to handle this stinking slimy mess. Adcock was a slippery operator. Nothing but actual, unmarked cash, in the great sum – in those days – of $500 was accepted. No checks, drafts or money orders, because they required receipt signatures. Once Adcock offered to lump in one grand steal, ten licensures for $3000.00 *cas*h. Some successful, prominent doctors paid much more. Adcock proved the whole mess was an A.M.A. conspiracy for he always delivered the license, duly signed by every member of an A.M.A. controlled Board.

"A few years later the medical goons in Chicago decided to make Adcock the 'goat' – throw him to the wolves. He was prosecuted and sent to prison. Game – he did not put the finger on his fellow criminal conspirators.

"The State Board – A.M.A. branded – next appointed one Dr. Horton, a Fellow A.M.A. He went 'hog wild' and accepted and endorsed checks for false licensures, and the whole putrid mess became public property. The A.M.A. Board got the jitters and refused to issue paid-for licenses. Previously the Board had been demanding blood and mud about the entrance credentials of applicants, so it made arrangements with school authorities to falsify the necessary credentials. Grammer school and later high school diplomas went like hot cakes at $100.00 to $300.00. Many young people, ambitious to become doctors, paid much more.

"Astute lawyers for the persecuted Medical Colleges filed documents in The Supreme Court of Missouri, exposing the whole system of bribery, extortions, purchase of credentials from A.M.A. members, means and amounts of money that changed hands. The Mephistophelean medical madmen in Chicago had complete punitive powers. *It did not exert them. Why?* It was proved that licenses by reciprocity were peddled in the K. C. Muelbach Hotel for $500.00 and a bottle of booze. The A.M.A. president of the Missouri Medical Society and Board of Health was an organizer and chief conspirator in this dirty, slimy chicanery. To repeat, he was president of the State Medical Society (A.M.A.) and of the Board of Health. God knows how many humans lost their lives because of the filthy crooks so licensed."

John looked up from the documented report of rascality and corruption to demand: "Dad, can there be any mistake? Can it be possible that the A.M.A. knew this but refused to rectify it? Doesn't the A.M.A. have full punitive powers to throw the scoundrels out of the Holy Art of Healing, regardless of the tag it bears?"

Pressing frowned as he replied: "Yes, it has far more power than it deserves. The A.M.A. could have rectified the matter within twenty-four hours. Knowing the Chicago gang as I do, there can be but one logical conclusion: the A.M.A. will not stop at any crime in its mad scramble for wealth and power. Let me show you proof." He arose, walked over, and opened his office safe. He held up pages of a newspaper. On them were two ads in bold, black type, stating that Dr. George H. Simmons (later owner of the A.M.A.) was a specialist in cancer cures and female complaints. The doctor remarked: "Son, Baron Munchausen never told such mendacities. The A.M.A. was organized to protect doctors against real quackery and poor drugs, as well as advertising medical rascals. The first thing Simmons did after he took over the A.M.A. was to issue a royal ukase that no doctor could advertise his healing art.

"And yet, this man had just graduated from lying, malicious, criminal advertising saying he could cure cancer. What A.M.A. doctor can say that he can cure cancer? But mark me, the day will come when someone, possibly a so-called charlatan, will find a positive cure. Then God help him, for organized medical banditry will mentally and psychologically crucify him – because of jealousy and misanthropy. Today what doctor can claim to cure that dreadful disease, or as many believe, syndrome or set of symptoms brought about by poor diet, malnutrition, poor elimination, and the chemicals man is now adopting in nutrition? I predict that the great killer disease will continue to increase as long as certain medical mountebanks hold the sway on the medical Olympus in Chicago. Now here is another ad stating that Simmons has just returned from post graduate courses in Europe. This was also proved untrue because Simmons had not been to Europe. He advertises that he is a Homeopathic physician. That, too, is very doubtful. It is said among A.M.A. doctors that he never graduated, and was granted the honorable title M.D. because of his position in the A.M.A.

"The enormous power he has allocated to himself and others in his charlatan class has put him and them in a position to be able to make any claim under the sun. It is most shocking to honest doctors – and there are thousands – to learn that such money-lusters get away with murder, malpractice, literally. Unquestionably Simmons' House of Health was a House of Hell, for it housed an abortion ring and a cancer cure fraud that put patients beyond any help but that of God."

"Does the A.M.A. still worship at Simmons' shrine of medical quackery?" asked John.

"Most certainly," replied the doctor, "and the commercial house organ of the A.M.A., called Journal, literally tears to shreds any physician or hospital that does not go under the yoke. Furthermore this commercial house Journal advertises junk in one decade and condemns the same junk in the next decade. Look over my files if you doubt it. It accepts and advertises new and untried, possibly harmful and toxic products – and I can name scores of them – marketed by large pharmaceutical makers. And this condition will grow worse until this despotism is destroyed. Why should we wonder at anything when such men as Simmons hold the scourge, through the Journal of which he is editor?"

"You know, John," continued Dr. Pressing, "every worthwhile thing must employ trial and error. That, son, is empiricism, the thing the A.M.A. damns. Every doctor uses empiricism, because he tries a remedy that he considers meets the indications, after a careful diagnosis, of course. If the medicine does not heal, the honest doctor admits the fact, and tries something else, because medicine may not work the same on two patients. The A.M.A. damns all this as empiricism, charlatanism and quackery – then does the same thing. How right was the Apostle Paul when he wrote: 'Thinkest thou, that judgest them that do these things, and doest the same, that thou shalt escape the Judgment of God?'

"By all means make a study of all means of healing, for you will need them. Future generations will arise and call you blessed. Son, I have factual evidence that only the body dies. The spiritual body marches right on in its evolution to perfection. What would Simmons not do to be able to return and undo, as far as possible, the evils he did in the flesh? I will write several letters for your future guidance in case I get the call. I wish you to learn *savatte*, *ju-jitsu* and *l'escrime,* also *le can* to be able always to protect yourself as a county General Practitioner — the very backbone of medicine. What do Simmons and his ilk know or care about driving twelve miles in mud to the horses' bellies, or wading through two feet of snow to care for a patient, after his Ford has broken down, or been buried in the snow? Neither of these two men have the least qualifications to head an organization that was founded for noble and glorious purposes, although now it is like any other despotism lusting for power and money. But as they continue to seize power, due to supine doctors and a Congress composed quite largely of lying lawyers, there will come a time, and not far off, when medical madmen will rule America with a rod of steel. That will come about too soon if young men like yourself do not become doctors and practice medicine in accordance with the Hippocratic Oath."

As Dr. Pressing stopped to take a breath, halting footsteps were heard slowly mounting the stairs. If one were to judge from the moans, someone was in unbearable pain. Dr. Pressing and John rushed to the outside office door and opened it.

A woman of about 45 years raised a ghastly face to them and gasped: "Please, oh please, help me."

She would have fallen if the two men had not caught her. They placed her gently on the old style Harvard table and Dr. Pressing asked: "You seem to be in severe pain. Where is it located?"

She feebly pointed to the lower right hand quadrant of the abdomen. "Right here. I can't stand it! For heaven's sake do something for me!" Another paroxysm doubled her up like a jack-knife and she fainted.

"John," said Dr. Pressing, "this a ruptured appendix, or I do not know medicine. I'll bet money some doctor prescribed a harsh laxative. She will die with peritionitis if she is not operated upon immediately. And we are going to do that appendectomy right here and now. Here, let's remove all her clothing below the waist. Spread a sheet over her except at McBurney's point. Then get washed up using German green soap. Re-sterilize all the instruments in the sterilizer. Then get a new can of ether and the mask."

At this point the women regained consciousness and demanded to know what was going on.

"You have an acute appendix and unless we operate, your life isn't worth a plugged nickel. Just take it easy for a few minutes while I take the case history and find out who you are and what is your name, and your relatives' names and addresses. I can take the information while my assistant is getting things ready."

The patient's acute pains had lessened quite a bit, but the doctor knew it would be for but a very short time. She gave her name, her brother's home address, where she was visiting.

"When did these cramps begin?" asked the doctor.

"Day before yesterday," she replied.

"Did you call any other doctor?"

"Yes, my brother called several doctors *but they would not come unless he guaranteed to have the money for the call before they entered the house.* Finally my brother went to a neighbor and borrowed the money for a call. Dr. Cheney came and *refused to help me until he collected in advance."*

"Did he make a thorough examination?"

"I do not know what you call thorough. He jerked back the covers, for I was in bed, and after punching away at the abdomen, said I had intestinal indigestion and ordered me to take two tablespoonsful of castor oil. Then he hurriedly left."

"Did your bowels move thoroughly?" asked the doctor.

"No, very little. Then these spasms came on. My brother was away from home so I walked over here. I thought I would die on the street."

CHAPTER 4

Throw physic to the dogs, I'll have none of it.

Dr. Pressing mentally ripped off a few choice expletives to fit the occasion. "Are you willing to have us remove the trouble?" he asked.

Just then she doubled up in agony and moaned: "Yes, do anything to stop this pain. And please hurry."

John hurried in from the small laboratory bearing all the equipment for an appendectomy.

"Start the ether, but administer it quite slowly," ordered the doctor, "while I wash up a bit and don rubber gloves. Make a small mouth and nose mask for me with a few folds of sterile gauze."

There was no reason to urge the patient to breath deeply, for it was anything, even death itself, to be free from the awful agony. The anesthetic dripped drop after drop and the woman became unconscious. Dr. Pressing came back to the operating table and John slipped the crude mask over his nose and mouth. Dr. Pressing took her pulse and then listened over the cardiac region and lungs.

"Strong as a horse," he observed. "I only pray that we do not get a peritonitis. Now, John, you watch her respiration and keep your finger on the pulse. I wish I could have had a little more time for a full examination, but these cases demand instant surgery. I have much to tell you about doctors who advise a violent purge when there is acute pain in the region of McBurney. And I also will give you much information on what we used to call 'kitchen' surgery. Every country G.P. who does not have a hospital for emergency cases must be ready to operate any time, any place – in a kitchen, or in the back yard in the shade of a tree. Well, here we go."

He again checked respiration and heart, then glanced sharply and appraisingly into John's eyes. "Son, are you up to this? It's going to be pretty rough going, but the life of a fellow being hangs in the balance, and God forgive us if we fail Him and her. We are now on O.M.S. – Our Master's Service. Let us not fail Him."

Without the batting of an eye, young John Marsh Pressing said: "Dad, after what I saw in my own former family I can take anything. I will not falter or fail, now or in the future in my duty as the kind of doctor I know you to be. Let's go."

As Dr. Pressing made the incision, he remarked: "Watch and pray, son, that the power of God will reinforce and sustain what little there is to medical science. Be sure and turn your face away if you should be forced to sneeze, or cough; however, I want you close enough to see every step. Now we are down to the muscles of the abdomen. Sponge! Hemostat! Sponge!"

Dr. Pressing worked without effort, but carefully. No grandstanding here! Just good, clean surgery. He resected the fasciae and divided the peritoneum, that marvelous sack that sustains the viscera of man. "Now we strip away the mesocolon, and there lies the appendix vermiformis. Thank God it has not ruptured yet.

"What prevented a rupture, with consequent peritonitis, must be God's intervention. Note this point, (pointing with the tip of the lancet) a sneeze would have probably done it. We won't have to worry about Fowler's position! Now clamp here, and here (again pointing) and clamp hard. Now note that I simply run the lancet between the two clamps and deliver to you the offending appendix. Now we pull tight the pursestring sutures. Sponge! Now swab the stump of the appendix with chinosol solution. Chinosol is the best and the safest antiseptic. Now we remove the other clamp. I'll tell you much about antiseptics and Lister later." He rapidly sutured the peritoneum, the muscular layer, the skin, sponged the trauma with chinosol solution, and put on a dry dressing.

"There you are, son, you have assisted in your first case of major surgery, and materially helped in saving a human life. Now, let's lift her from the table and place her on that couch. She may have some nausea, maybe not, as she comes from under the anesthetic. Post-operative vomiting is a nasty mess, but cannot be avoided in many cases. While we sit here and wait, let me give you some information that proves that medical monopoly, wherever and whenever encountered, has been on all sides of all questions, and far too often wrong. Can you imagine doing this bit of surgery without antiseptics, or anaesthesia? And yet, organized medicine fought both techniques bitterly!"

John asked: "Are you serious? Is it possible that men sworn under the Hippocratic Oath fought against medical progress?"

"Yes, they did. When Lister conceived that millions of deaths were due to some unknown element residing in pus, filth and the like, and began employing carbolic acid as an antiseptic, he was publicly denounced by the medical profession. He also was the first physician who insisted on boiling the surgical instruments, as well as inventing absorbable sutures, such as we just used. He also invented several new surgical instruments such as the sinus forceps. Post operative deaths dropped 70% when he operated. Nevertheless, he was persecuted by unconscionable medical doctors."

"Where did Lister get his ideas that micro-organisms were the causes of sickness and death?" asked John.

"He arrived at his correct conclusions by following the work of Pasteur, the great French bacteriologist, whose work saved the French wine industry from extinction. Pasteur was not a Doctor of Medicine, so, naturally, that crowd persecuted him as if he was the most malignant scoundrel on the planet. Pasteur saved the wine and silk industry through his discoveries in bacteriology. He produced anti-rabic vaccine and an anthrax vaccine. Both have saved uncounted lives. Son, I find it most difficult to fathom the depths of degradation that medicine has often exhibited. A man makes a marvelous life-saving discovery. Then the very creatures, not men surely, who have sworn to save lives – never take them – fight the discovery and the discoverer tooth and toenail. Hundreds of thousands of women were dying from puerperal sepsis, childbed fever. The doctors went on their merry way, letting them die. Dr. Oliver Wendel Holmes, a great doctor as well as author and poet, conceived that puerperal sepsis was caused by bacteria, and said so. The medical monopoly nearly blew him out of the water. He was persecuted and abused by graduate doctors as if he was a pickpocket. But he won out finally because:

" 'Truth crushed to earth shall rise again,
The eternal years of God are hers.
While error, wounded, writhes in pain,
And dies among her worshippers.' "

"Wasn't it Dr. Holmes who said: 'If all the medicine in the world was cast into the sea, it would be that much better off for mankind, and that much worse for the fish.'? I seem to remember having read that somewhere."

"Right you are. And he also gave us another great truism: 'Science is the topography of ignorance.' Get a basin, son, for I see that our patient is beginning to come from under the ether. Now she had dropped back under again." He took her pulse, passed his stethoscope over her entire body and nodded his head in satisfaction. The patient began to pass explosive gas from the bowel. Finally the bowel moved and John got his first experience in cleaning up a real mess. Fortunately, Dr. Pressing had placed protective rubber sheeting and plenty of absorptive material under the buttocks.

"She is coming along fine, and I actually believe she is not going to be much nauseated.

"Now, speaking about anesthesia. The ancient Incas of Peru did massive brain surgery, employing the leaves of a plant called erythroxylon coca, from which our modern drug cocaine is obtained. Inca surgeons used no antiseptics that we know of; the incision was made with sharp flint knives; the anaesthetic was used by chewing the leaves and spitting the medicated saliva into the area. The technique was quite successful, as to this day many skulls are found showing the healed cranial sutures. They had no high-fallutin' medical jargon, no medical trust, and yet, these supposedly ignorant Indians in the high Andes discovered one of the most valuable medicinal agents the world has ever known. I am speaking of cinchona rubra, from which we obtain quinine."

The patient opened her eyes and stirred slightly, then dropped back into unconsciousness. Dr. Pressing again took her pulse, used his stethoscope over lungs and heart, nodded his head as if he was well satisfied with the situation. He then continued with his lecture. "There is good evidence that Cro-Magnon man of perhaps 30,000 B.C. did trephines, employing flint saws and drills to open the skull. The earliest Hebrews did circumcisions employing flint knives. Our authorities tell us that ancient Hindus did massive major surgery, employing the juice of papaver somniferum (opium) to deaden pain. The early Greeks and Romans did fine surgery employing bronze instruments, with excellent results."

"How did they avoid surgical infections?" asked John.

"They washed out the wounds with boiled water and strong wine, so say those who have made a study of the matter. When Pompeii was excavated, magnificent surgical instruments of bronze were found. I have seen two large collections of these instruments. As man made progress in what he called civilization, and large towns sprang up, before the days of sewers and other means of sanitation, infections became more in evidence. I think, as do many real authorities, that man shut off the healing, antiseptic rays of Old Sol to his own destruction. The ancient Greeks and Romans anointed their bodies with pure olive oil and then sun bathed. Mammoth pelvic and abdominal wound cases were exposed to pure sunlight, and healed. Someday some worthwhile young doctor is going to tell us the why of this. And another thing, John, it was discovered in the Gran Chaco War in South America, as well as in our Civil War, that when a serious wound was blown by flies, and the trauma filled with maggots, the wound healed much more rapidly. When some God-gifted young doctor finds the solution, and announces it, the medical monopoly will make his life a living hell."

(Author's note: Some years after Dr. Pressing's prediction, it was proved that the maggots secreted, or caused the broken down tissues to synthesize a substance called Allantoin, that was later synthetically produced. Morris Fishbein, then the Czar of the A.M.A., called the discovery the 'best laugh of the year.' In justice to Fishbein, let it be said that he got religion, or something, and began telling the true facts about the A.M.A. He was promptly placed on a large pension and the A.M.A. knew him no more. Query. Why has so-called scientific medicine forever waged war to the knife on any and every system that tends to prevent or heal? I think so often of that Latin adage, *Ubi tres Medici, ibi duo Athei.* As an Atheist does not believe in the survival of man, it naturally follows that they are untrustworthy and undependable.

When the author was reading medicine, he had many opportunities of observing medical students' attempts to 'harden themselves' by the most brutal and bestial conduct toward the corpses that had once been the 'Temple of a Soul.' I said, "brutal and bestial," and I mean exactly what I said – BRUTAL AND BESTIAL. As many of the cadavers for dissection were 'body snatched', who can surely say that his own mother or sister were not subjected to practices most vile and damnable. What a hopeful sign it is that many modern surgeons seek the help of God in their work. But how sad to remember that there are so very few of them.)

Dr. Pressing continued: "Can you imagine doing this laparotomy without a quick anaesthetic, John? And yet both church and so-called medical science fought anaesthesis. The church held that it was not Christlike to attempt to prevent pain. The medical men fought the use of ether because it was first demonstrated by Dr. Morton, a dentist, not by an A.M.A. doctor.

"My son, the greatest scientists who ever lived have offered overwhelming evidence that man just cannot die. That his spiritual body just steps out of the old diseased mass of clay and lives on. Man has to be disciplined after death for the crimes he did before passing on. Remind me to hand you Sir William Crookes' marvelous revelation. The reason I bring this up is this: If a man's spirit, after death, is thoroughly disciplined for the sins and crimes committed during his physical life, what will be the penalty on doctors who have taken the Hippocratic Oath and foresworn themselves?

"Assuming that all survive, what will these doctors foresworn say to Hippocrates? To Galen? To the great surgeons and physicians of the Alexandrian Medical School? That reminds me: never use any product made from coal tar, antipyrine (that killed thousands) acetanilid (ditto thousands), phenacetin (ditto thousands). As far as possible, use God's kind of medicine – faith and the botanical plants he has given His children for the healing of the nations. And for humanity's sake, do all you can to suppress this thing of self-diagnosis and treatment. Franklin said: "He that dopes himself has a fool for patient.' Hand me down that small red book up there, the next to the last book on the upper shelf."

He took the book and rapidly thumbed the pages until he came to this statement by Dr. Adam Smith: "After denouncing Paracelsus as a quack, the regular medical profession stole his 'quack-silver' – mercury; after persecuting Jenner as an imposter it adopted his discovery of vaccination; after dubbing Harvey a humbug it was forced to swallow his theory of the circulation of the blood." Professor C. W. Emerson, M.D. wrote: "The progress in medicine has and continues to come from the unlearned. Common people give us our improvements and the school men spend their time in giving Latin and Greek names to these improvements."

(Author's note: The Greeks, the Romans as well as the Japanese, attributed a great deal of their well being to massage and physical manipulation. When Dr. Sill brought forth a very valuable modality in Osteopathy, the A.M.A. could not find words sufficiently bitter in the dictionary. Osteopathy made good, nevertheless. When Palmer conceived that nerve impingement in the spine was a major cause of ill health, the medical maligners invented new words of ridicule, damning him a fish monger.)

As Dr. Pressing stopped to take breath, John said: "I'll swear to one thing, Dad: I'm going to study all schools of healing, and I am going to use everything that will benefit my patients."

The patient opened both eyes and asked: "Where am I?"

Dr. Pressing replied: "You are all right. You are in Dr. Pressing's office. Don't you remember that awful pain? Have you any pain now?"

The patient murmured: "No, there is no pain anywhere now, thank heaven. No one will know how I suffered. Will you please send word to my brother so he can come for me?"

"Yes, I will send my assistant for him. But you cannot be moved tonight. Perhaps tomorrow we can fix up some way to get you home. I will call a practical nurse to come and stay with you until you can be moved safely."

"May I have a drink of water?" asked the patient.

"Not tonight, but I will have my assistant bring some ice and you may hold some small slivers in your mouth. That will allay your thirst." Turning to John he said: "See if you can find her brother and then get Mrs. Howe to come over to sit with her all night. Get that bed pan off the top shelf so it will be ready if needed. And be sure to save that infected appendix to show to her folks. Drop it in a wide mouth vial and pour alcohol in it."

John hastened away to attend to his duties, and Dr. Pressing settled down to watch his patient. There was little nausea and no vomiting. She attempted to talk, but Dr. Pressing told her to lie very quiet, relax and try to go to sleep. The doctor took down a large medical directory and began making notes on a scrap of paper. Dr. Pressing knew the name of the supposed medical scientist who had practically sentenced a fellow being to death by ordering a harsh cathartic in an acute appendix.

About two hours later, at 6:30 P.M., John returned with the patient's brother and the practical nurse. After giving the nurse instructions – from past experiences with her, the doctor knew that few directions were required – he and John drove toward home and supper.

Mrs. Pressing had been a doctor's helpmate far too long to wonder at anything. She knew that a decent, honest doctor's time belonged to suffering humanity. Furthermore, she knew that the silliest woman on earth was the doctor's wife who entertained jealousy, for a doctor is accustomed to seeing a lot of anatomy, both male and female. The fine points of any woman, other than the woman who had stuck to him like a cockle burr in a dog's tail, had no allurements or temptations for him. Medical examination of women serves as the best anaphrodisiac.

"My," she said. "You boys look all tuckered out. What have you been up to?"

"We had an emergency appendectomy at the office, Mother. John was my assistant, and I tell you he is going to make one of the greatest doctors in the country. He will be great because he is prepared already to do better work than half the interns in the great hospitals. In addition, he has nerves of steel. And we know he is absolutely honest, a rara avis, indeed, these days. One thing only I fear – that he will be just too good to stay in a small town on a general practitioner's job. Say, what's cookin'? Chicken and dumplings or I had better get to a nose specialist."

His diagnosis being proved right, they washed up and sat down to a real, country style supper.

"Now boys, we just won't have any shop talk, so let's talk of your future, John. Too soon you will be going to take your pre-med. I notice that you do not seem at all interested in girls, but some female society would be good for you. You must not make a slave of yourself in your education. 'All work and no play makes Jack a dull boy,' you know. What do you think, Pa?"

"Mother, that is up to John. He has great equilibrium and a rare sense of honor and justice. Leave it all up to him."

Painful memories slipped momentarily from John's superconscious mind to his conscious mind, for his brow furrowed and there was an indescribable glint of pain in his eyes. He said: "For reasons you understand, I think I shall never love and marry any woman. For many years I heard nothing but quarrelling and fighting. Added to that I saw so-called scientific medical doctors cut, slash and burn my mother. Yet, I know that there are honest doctors, those who reject the yoke that medical despotism, brutality and chicanery would load on their necks.

"I have talked to quite a number of doctors, unknown to you dear folks, and little as I yet know of the healing arts, I still know that other than medical doctors possess unquestionable means of preventing, or healing diseases. I expect to meet many more doctors, of different schools, while at the same time I shall not neglect the fact that the Book quite evidently points out that the really specific medicines are to be found, and will continue to be found, in the things that God grows for the healing of the nations, the botanicals."

"Son, we are forbidden to talk shop this evening, but tomorrow, if we have time, I want to bring out the skeleton in our closet, a real skeleton that I have at the office. I want to drill you most thoroughly on the vertebra and point out the possibilities that it is probable that many diseases are caused by what is called a subluxation, and how it may bring pressure on certain important nerves and thus unfavorably affect vital organs such as the stomach, the gall bladder, the heart, the intestines, the sex organs, in fact, any of the structures with the possible exception of the brain."

"I suppose you are speaking of Osteopathy and Chiropractic," said John. "I have read strong condemnations of both these forms of treatment in your Journal of the A.M.A. How about them?"

Dr. Pressing replied with some heat: "John, the great poet Dryden once wrote:

" 'He'd rather far that I should die
Than his prediction prove a lie.'

Of course Dryden referred to his doctor's diagnosis. I have many times quoted that passage from the N.Y. Medical Journal: 'It is better to see a patient die under Allopathy than to see his life saved under Homeopathy.' Some doctors are so pig-headed and filled with jealousy and misanthropy, they lose sight of the glory of the healing arts. I once knew a doctor in Oklahoma who told me personally: 'I wish one of those traveling harlot vans would come to town so I could get a lot of venereal cases to treat.' Well, sir, a short time later his wish was fulfilled in a way he did not like. His only son got a rampant case of Neisserian infection. He infected his wife. A baby came in due time with ophthalmia neonatorum. The attending physician, one of those brass plated A.M.A. doctors, did not use Crede' solution, and the poor child is now in a blind asylum.

"Both the man and his wife have spent a fortune and were not cured. Both have gonorrheal arthritis and hobble around town with canes. I can recount hundreds of such cases. And the A.M.A. ignores such evil doctors right down the line. Some of the most vicious abortionists, some of the rottenest fee splitters and fee gougers, are great Association members and the most virulent in their criminal condemnation of any form of healing that does not have the blessing of the American Medical Association hierarchy in Chicago. A misnomer, for it is not American and it is not real medicine.

"I knew Dr. Sill and I know that he got results with manipulation after medicine had signally failed. I have read circulars sent out by organized medical greed, making all sorts of innuendoes against Chiropractic and they declared Palmer was a fish monger. Let me again repeat that Jesus Christ chose, by preference, fishermen to become fishers of men. And his fishermen's names will be blessed on the lips of decent humans as long as one of them lives. And speaking about fish, there is a man in the A.M.A. who never practiced a day in his life. He never had a patient. He is being groomed to succeed that awful quack, Simmons, when Simmons is called to an accounting he won't like. That man's name is Morris Fishbein. The world will not fail to remember that the A.M.A. also has fish in its locker. Just wait a few years, my boy; for the man is a clever organizer, a keen thinker, ruthless in his methods against what he calls 'quacks'. But he talks too much and some of these days he is going to open his mouth too wide and get his foot caught in it. Then he will be a scapegoat."

(Author: I have a bale of references to confirm the prediction made by Dr. Pressing some 30 years ago. In justice to Fishbein, let it be said that after he had been suddenly retired to close his mouth [on a great pension you may be sure], he came out in active condemnation against the political chicanery of A.M.A. and against a lot of these new 'blunder' drugs. Therefore, Morris Fishbein, I salute you now for something you should have done many, many years ago. But why the change of heart? Honesty? Revenge? Jealousy? Only God and you can answer that, Sir. And I'm like the Quaker: "Friend, every man but thee and me are innate liars. And here of late I have found it isn't me." Friend Morris, let us hope that you repent and show deeds of repentance regarding your persecution of other than A.M.A. standards before you are called to the last round-up.)

Mother Pressing closed the discussion. "You boys get to bed right now. Nobody can predict when a G.P. has to get up and go. I'll wager you will get an O.B. call before morning."

CHAPTER 5

Mother Pressing was a good prophet. At 4 A.M. sharp the beat of hooves was heard drumming down the main street. A few minutes later someone hammered on the Pressing front door as if he had brought one of Julius Caesar's battering rams along with him. Young John Marsh Pressing was the first to get to the door and found two things, a young man of about 23, soaking wet; and worse yet it was raining like the proverbial cats and dogs.

"Dr. Pressing?" he gasped.

The doctor answered for himself just back of John: "Yes, I am Dr. Pressing. What emergency brings you out at this time of night and a torrent to boot? Step inside and tell me your trouble."

"It's my wife. She is trying to have a baby and it just won't come. Her mother is a mid-wife and urged me to get a regular doctor. Will you please come at once?"

"Where do you live? I do not seem to know you."

The man replied: "We have just moved into the Strong farm down below Steinmetz."

"That is rather out of my territory and, furthermore, we would have to cross that rickety old bridge over Cedar Creek. It was condemned years ago as hazardous and now with this cloudburst, it's worth a man's life to cross it. Glasgow is on your side of the creek and you should have called one of the Glasgow doctors."

"I rode to Glasgow and called three doctors but not one of them would come. One said he would come if I had fifty dollars to pay on the barrel head. I haven't that kind of money now, but soon will have. Two other doctors were out on call, their wives said, but I happen to know better. Dr. S. . . . is sitting in on a poker game at the drug store. The night marshal told me he positively would not make calls from sundown to sun up. Won't you please come?"

The pleading look on the man's face settled it with Dr. Pressing. It reminded him of the eyes of the dog he had owned in his youth that had saved his life when a panther attacked the sprouting young hunter. "John," he ordered, "get the team harnessed. No car could make it in these horrible, bottomless roads. I will get my OB bag ready while mother makes us some boiling hot coffee." (His nose must have been good for the aroma of fresh boiling Java was already coming from the kitchen.)

The doctor checked thoroughly the contents of his OB bag and had Mother Pressing re-boiling several instruments, which he hoped prayerfully he would not need. Delivery forceps were almost as unnatural, in his belief, as a lot of un-needed surgery going the rounds.

John came in to report the rig was ready, the three men drank two cups each of coffee strong enough to leach metal and then pulled on rubber boots and slickers. The man on the horse lead the way. There was one flash of lightning after another. The thunder was incessant, making it impossible to hold conversation. In many spots the buggy wheels sank until the hubs dragged the mud. Dr. Pressing was extremely worried about crossing Cedar Creek Bridge. But human lives were at stake. He must not and he would not fail.

(Author: Floods, fires, blizzards, cyclones were all the same to the those noble early physicians who did not need, did not want, very often abhorred the medical societies that had already begun to show the wolf beneath the sheep's skin, in foul deeds of non-Hippocratic medical moneyitis! Of course doctors had to live just as they do today. And, as says Holy Writ: "The laborer is worthy of his hire." John Marsh Pressing was to learn plenty about the medical societies and their money-mad mother as you, too, shall learn, or possibly already know. He was to discover, by actual experience, what you may have observed – ghost surgery, kick backs, unnecessary surgery for the benefit of foresworn doctors of medicine. Kick backs?

Yes, from surgeons, druggists, surgical instrument makers, pharmaceutical houses, optometrists; in truth, perhaps in the not distant future, *many doctors will be demanding kick backs from morticians.* From information given by the great gynecologist, Dr. H. [name on request] it seems very probable that many doctors hold stock in large pharmaceutical houses such as Parke Davis, Eli Lily, Sharpe & Doame, John Wyeth. It might be of great interest to know, under oath, if some doctors did not demand and receive stock for boosting more or less questionable products. The writer has documentary evidence of doctors who demanded and received physical therapy apparatus amounting to fantastic sums for plugging certain gadgets. [Documentary evidence available]. There are tens of thousands of honest, conscientious men engaged in the healing arts. The author will quote many of them as and after John Marsh Pressing learns of the heights and the depths of medicine.)

After nearly two hours of fighting hub-deep mud, they arrived at the questionable bridge. The patient's husband rode ahead and examined it. It was shaky but just how much so, only Providence knew. Dr. Pressing had a plan which was carried out: The horses were detached from the buggy and led, one at a time, over the bridge. The buggy, minus passengers, was then drawn slowly across it. The horses were again harnessed to the buggy, the doctor and John took their seat, and in another twenty minutes they reached their destination. They were met at the door by the patient's mother, a handsome, healthy specimen about fifty years old.

"How is Ethel?" demanded the husband before she could utter a word.

"Nothing has happened yet. She lies there actually holding back the pains. Ethel is a good girl – but spoiled rotten. If we can make her fighting mad, she will get down to business and the baby will come on the double."

"Just what do you mean?" asked the doctor.

"I mean, if you approve, to give my son-in-law Old Harry. She will be furious and the pains will increase and the baby come."

Dr. Pressing grinned and said: "I have known this to happen before. I knew one mother that slapped her daughter in the face with a splat that could have been heard a hundreds rods away. Let us see the patient first. If it seems the thing to do, I will nod to you." He looked at the young husband. "Is this all right with you?"

"Anything to get it over with," replied the husband.

They entered the bedroom. The husband walked over and kissed his wife and asked how she felt.

"Rotten, thanks to you," she snapped. An expulsive pain struck her and she palpably held it back. She gasped and snapped insults at her unoffending husband. The pain let up and she wailed dismally: "Just see what you have done to me. Just like a darn man. I wish I had never met you. . . . "

Dr. Pressing made every effort to gain her co-operation, without avail. The doctor-to-be John Marsh Pressing made a solemn oath in his mind that there would be no wedding bells for him. Never and two centuries added. With the exception of the Pressings, the samples of married life he had encountered to date were more than enough. The wife continued to moan and bewail the lot of women in general, herself in particular.

Dr. Pressing glanced at her mother and nodded his head. The dear old mother caught her cue and began running down her son-in-law. She walked close to the side of her daughter's bed and remarked: "Well, Mary-quite-contrary, Dad and I told you what your life would be with this bum you just had to have. His family never was much. He is far less much. As soon as you get over this, Dad and I are going to start annulment proceedings, and we will get it, too, for Dad throws a lot of weight around the county seat. You just wait, young lady. We will put up his brat for adoption. If we don't get you freed, this thing will happen again and again. I know this Vance family. Just women-chasers every one of them. . . "

Mary's face lit up like a Christmas tree and her eyes snapped as if she had a Winshurst plate machine back in her superconscious mind. The tactic had worked.

"I'm a Vance now, ma, and the Vances are every bit as good as the Welch family! I am over age and you are not running my affairs. I loved John, married him, and we are staying married. Now you get out of here." The older lady sniffed, looked at Dr. Pressing, secretively winked an eye and grinned, then left the room. Instead of holding back, Mary was now forcing the expulsive efforts. In twenty minutes, the doctor held up a fine boy baby by the heels and gave him just one spat on the buttocks. He shrieked lustily at his first spanking and the doctor handed him over to his grandmother for his first bath.

The young husband followed them into the next room and kissed the old lady lustily. "Mother, you are a pal," he said.

Meantime, Dr. Pressing, ably aided by John, examined the new mother and found a cicatrix (scar) that looked like some pork butcher had done surgery on her. The placenta came away and the new mother dropped off to a well-earned slumber. On going into the next room to examine the new baby, Dr. Pressing asked about that jagged scar. It seemed that some over-zealous young doctor, who imagined he was a surgeon because he had had four years of medicine and one year of internship, had so vigorously urged that, if this girl's ovaries were not taken out, the consequence might be most deplorable. The parents agreed to surgery and it was done under the very questionable environment of a fire-trap hospital, poorly trained doctor and nurses. The parents nor the patient had never seen the supposedly removed glands. It was very evident that the parts had never been removed, as was proved by the fact that she had married, become enciente and born a baby. It was without doubt an operation performed on the purse of the parents.

(Author: Even A.M.A doctors, those who are honest, admit thousands of such cases!)

Dr. Pressing muttered something to himself and then closed up like a clam. Shortly after daybreak the storm ceased. The two Pressing 'boys' had little difficulty in avoiding bad spots, and reached home safely, primed and ready for the sausage, buckwheats and strong coffee that Mother Pressing set on the table in less than half an hour. The doctor held his righteous indignation until he and his adopted son had reached the office. He was usually a man of even disposition and tried to live a decent Christian life. However, and he should not be condemned, he did give way to some language that would not have met the approval of his clergyman. He cooled off after the safety valve had released the super-pressure and remarked to John: "These are the sort of things you are going to meet with more and more as you go along. The disease of Easy Moneyitis is almost epidemic since Simmons took over the A.M.A.

"However, I have hopes that that organization will go to hell along with the butchers who have blackened the pages of history. I believe it is the Law of God that every despotism, and despot shall perish and be only remembered with execration."'

Footsteps were now to be heard falteringly mounting the stairs to the office. The door slowly opened and a husky man of about twenty-five came in. "Doctor," he said, "I want you to take a look at my leg. Two doctors say I have a bone cancer and want to take off my leg above the knee. Another doctor said it was nothing but a skin cancer and advised against surgery. He said if I did have surgery, the thing might spread to other portions of my body and then nothing would save my life."

He was brought in and placed on the Harvard table, then Dr. Pressing rolled up the patient's pants leg and removed the pus-stained crude dressing.

It was a rather ghastly sore that lay exposed. The doctor examined it long and carefully before saying a word. Apparently satisfied with what he saw, he took the man's case history. Name: James Smith. Age: 26. Trade or profession: railroad fireman. Cause of condition: jumped from a running railroad engine to avoid taking a minor part in a cornfield meet.

"When did it happen?" asked the doctor.

"Two weeks ago yesterday."

"Why didn't you go to the railroad company hospital?"

"I did go and the doctors and surgeon could not agree on a diagnosis. I know a good many 'rails' that those sawbones have worked over, and the patients always came out second best," replied Jim Smith. "Is it a cancer?"

"I am not one of those brass plated specialists, but have seen a good many real cancers here and in Europe where I took some post graduate work. I do not think it is cancerous. Let's take your temperature." It proved to be 100°, about 1½° above normal. "It seems to me you have nothing but an infection with plenty of what you call proud flesh. I make no promises, but if you can come to see me every day for a while, and will submit to the treatment I shall outline, I think we can clear this up. If you have confidence in me and what I do, we will start at once."

The man agreed heartily. Dr. Pressing then took a medical book from the shelves and read and described the natural use of maggots, from the blow fly, to clear up such cases.

"That sounds pretty darn severe, but I'll go along with you. When do we start?"

"Suppose John finds you a room here in town for a few days, so I can keep in touch. Agreeable?"

It being agreeable, John found the room and took Smith to it. It was a nice room on the first floor and had a large, grassy back yard – just what the doctor ordered.

After the patient was settled, the doctor sent John to

find some blow flies. He placed them in a drinking glass and held the open end of the glass down over the sore. The flies immediately began working on the spot and Dr. Pressing ordered the patient to sit where the wound would be exposed to the direct rays of Old Sol. In due time the lesion was filled with healing maggots that ate away all the broken down tissues and synthesized a product that began the healing process as if by magic. The trauma began to heal from the bottom. Healthy granulations formed and grew. In ten days the supposed cancer was entirely filled in and nothing showed but a healthy scab. In another week nothing showed but a pink scar. Nature healed the wound and Dr. Pressing collected a fee of $20.00. This was not ten per cent of what the patient would have paid in a hospital. And he had a good leg instead of a stump.

In the meantime, medical practice was brisk and Dr. Pressing and John were busy although the acute paucity of physicians was not nearly as great then as it is now. Dr. Callous had been very busy, too, as he went about attending medical society meetings, condemning charlatans and quacks, and doing abortions on a wholesale basis. Dr. Pressing was called twice to clean up messes, left by Callous. The County Medical Society was duly informed – and did nothing. Nothing punitive, that is. Dr. Callous grinned behind his sprouting whiskers as he clinked gold in his pockets. (Author: This is no fiction. The author personally knows of dozens, possibly hundreds of criminal abortions performed by this great apostle of scientific medicine. Two were the author's own two sisters-in-law.

Regarding the maggot treatment, it had been used with real success many years before the days of John Marsh Pressing. A number of years after the case of Jim Smith, the man who claimed to be a physician and the ringmaster in the A.M.A. circus, Morris Fishbein, heard of this type of treatment and called it "the laugh of the year."

Shortly thereafter, the *Pathfinder Magazine* ran a story about Allontoin, the substance synthesized by maggots in wounds. The story bore the title, IS DR. FISHBEIN'S FACE RED? It surely was. Mr. Fishbein constantly brags about 'scientific' medicine. There is no such thing as medical science. If there were, every doctor's first diagnosis would be correct, and every patient would soon recover his health, or die, Yes:

"He'd rather far that I should die
Than his prediction prove a lie." – Dryden.

You go to a physician. If he is an honest doctor he will get your family history, make a careful examination employing his four necessary physical senses, use the discoveries that have come down through the ages from masters of medicine. He may prescribe what he considers the remedy. But suppose the medicine does not cure you? What then? He studies your symptoms more closely. He prescribes something else. In other words he is what Mr. Fishbein claims to abhor and despise, an empiric, a charlatan, a quack. No honest and wise man denies that the healing arts, regardless of the school, are the noblest and finest gifts of God to man. After all the word science means 'that which is known', not 'that which I think'. The long rugged history of the world proves that the science of one generation is usually to be found in the garbage heap of the next generation.

When a doctors' trade union, not one connected with trade unions of workers striving to better themselves and receive a fair share of the wealth they produce, allocates to itself the prerogatives of our merciful Creator, and seeks to pick the purses of people, it is more than high time that that sort of union be placed under the laws of God and of men. Any medical trade union that seeks to sanctify and protect kick backs, splitting of fees, unnecessary surgery done at highbinder fees and done by inept surgeons, ghost surgery and other means of raping the rabble, the Public must arise and destroy such a trade union of doctors, and set up again the semi-divine Oath of Hippocrates. And always thereafter keep its ears to the ground.

The doctor-to-be, John Marsh Pressing, will discover these crimes against God and his favorite creatures, Man, as he is now prepared to begin that six-year grind to gain the much coveted degree of Physician and Surgeon plus a wide knowledge of other forms of healing.)

CHAPTER 6

Physician, heal thyself

"And a certain woman which had an issue of blood twelve years. And suffered many things of many physicians, and had spent all that she had, and was nothing bettered, but rather grew worse." Mark 5:30.

It was just a month before John was to matriculate in his pre-medic course. Every day he had been working on all sorts of cases with a past master in medicine, Dr. Pressing. The doctor called John into his private office and said: "John, I feel sure that you wish to become a doctor *par excellence*. You will need some proved form of exercise that combines with it a sure means of defense. Therefore, I wish you to leave for Chicago tomorrow and contact two specialists whom I know personally. One is a master of *ju-jitsu*. The other a master of the French system of defense, the *savate*, or boxing with the feet. As you know, the leg muscles are many times stronger than the muscles of the arms. In a month you should be well-trained in these two forms of exercise and defense.

"Let me give you an example. The last time I was in Paris, I saw a burly beer drayman attack, for no known good reason, a smallish looking man who was dressed in a foppish manner. He carried a very light malacca walking stick. Believe me it was not an ornament. The large brute rushed at him as if he meant to tear the smallish party into tatters. The small one seemed to poise all his body in a relaxed state. He even smiled a bit, a very pleasant smile. As the brute drew back his mighty fist to launch a knockdown blow, the small man simply kicked his apponent's patella with his sharp-toed boot. The bully started to fall forward. With the speed of light the savate boxer kicked him in the solar plexus region, and, as the bully continued toward the hard pavement, the savate boxer jerked up his knee striking the other's forehead. The man dropped unconscious to the pavement.

"Three of the bully's friends rushed in to pulverize the dandy. A pleasant smile never left his face as he started to use that little wisp of a cane. With its tip he punched one foe's Adam's apple. He whipped his stick around striking the other two combatants below the ear. In less time than it took me to tell you this, four very much injured Frenchmen were groaning on the cold cobblestones. About *ju-jitsu:* there are certain holds when at close quarters to tame anybody who does not know the Japanese art of defense. Expert *ju-jitsu* wrestlers have information about nerve centers and bone and skeletal structures that is little known among Western peoples. Dr. Kuwashimo is under some obligations to me — at least he says so — and he will really teach you the art of self-defense at close quarters. Professor Lavoisier will teach you what to do when not in close contact.

"As you go along in medicine you will find great use for both systems. In the handling of the insane for instance. . . "

The conversation was interrupted at that moment by footsteps rushing up the stairs. A girl of some 18 years, panting violently, rushed into the outer office screaming: "Dr. Pressing, Dr. Pressing, come quickly. Dr. Callous is dying!" Dr. Pressing and John opened the door and confronted the panting maiden. They recognized her as the eldest daughter of Dr. Callous.

"What happened to the doctor?" asked Dr. Pressing.

"He was shot with a shotgun by Jed Miller. Miller claims that Dr. Callous killed his sister by an unlawful act. But hurry, doctor, and try to save my Dad."

Dr. Pressing had for a long time suspected that this very thing would happen. He knew and the County Medical Society knew what this man had been doing for a number of years. And yet he was not thrown out of organized medicine, nor had he ever been punished by man's sort of justice. Dr. Callous lived only a matter of two city blocks from the Pressing office so Dr. Pressing and John followed the girl rapidly to the residence of Dr. Callous. They went into the bedroom to behold a situation that every doctor hopes he will never meet – the final hours of a confessed Atheist, plus a man who was a disgrace to the healing arts.

Just the day before this affair, Dr. Pressing and John had passed the top of the day to Callous on the street. He then appeared to be in the pink of health. His clothes fitted him as if the man had been melted and poured into his dashing raiment. He was gay, debonaire and apparently happy with his type of life. Now, all gay raiment removed and exsanguinated, he lay in his bed the picture of dissolution, his face as white as the snows on Everest, his eyes bearing the stamp of despair. Dr. Pressing rapidly turned back the covers, removed the crude dressing and looked at a fatal wound – not a doubt about it. The gaping hole left by a full charge of buckshot exposed a liver torn to shreds. The colon, at the hepatic flexure, was practically torn in twain. The man must have had a better than usual coagulative power of the blood for heavy clots had practically stopped the hemorrhage. Any attempt to clean up the trauma and dress it would mean, thought Dr. Pressing, that the patient would bleed to death in a matter of minutes.

Fortunately, or perhaps not, Dr. Callous was conscious, and, despite the lessened blood supply to the brain, his mind was remarkably clear. "What are my chances?" he whispered. "I want the facts right from the shoulder."

"No use to try and deceive you. You know as I know that you have at best less than two hours. Shall we send for a minister?" replied Dr. Pressing.

"No use," replied Callous. "Will you stay with me until the end? Please do. I am so afraid. I now know," he whispered in a weakening tone, "what many of my patients felt when they knew they were dying. Dr. Pressing, this shows the final scene in a man's life who made money and power his God." He paused and gasped for breath.

Dr. Pressing drew a chair up to the bedside and gently replaced the dressings he had so lately removed. Then he reached out and held the dying man's hand.

Dr. Callous opened his eyes and rolled them around, for he was too weak to turn his head.

"Dr. Pressing, is there a God? Is this form I loved so dearly soon to become nothing but a mass of chemicals? If one survives, what hope is there for one who has done what you know I have been doing for the last twenty years?"

Dr. Pressing pressed the hand of one who was going to find out the facts first hand in a very short time. He took the dying man's pulse. It was hardly detectable. His respiration was now Cheynne-Stokes. There was carphology. If he was going to do anything for this person, he knew it was going to have to be done in a very few minutes. "My friend, the Book says: 'The fool hath said in his heart that there is no God.' When I was taking some P.G. in Vienna, an aspirant to Atheism asked our instructor in mental disease if there was a God. The instructor glanced about him meditatively for a few moments, then snapped: 'Any man who observes the way a man is put together, any man who walks about on a clear Autumn night and sees the millions of stars and planets floating in space, without any visible means of support, every body moving in its orbit and never a collision; I say that any man who looks at these things and denies the Intelligence we know as God, that man I say *ist ein verdamtes dumnkopf.*' Dr. Callous, he was so very, very wise. There is a God, a kind, loving Creator."

Dr. Callous moaned in a voice so low he could hardly be heard: "Doctor, will you say a short prayer for me. Oh, God, how I need mercy."

"I'll do even better. I will give you the Publican who beat his breast and called: 'Oh God, be merciful to me, a sinner.' Jesus said that he was justified. Repeat over and over: 'God have mercy on me, a sinner.' Hold on to that thought as long as your mind can think it. 'God have mercy on me, a sinner.'"

Dr. Callous opened his eyes with what seemed a superhuman effort and looked his gratitude at one he had formerly considered a back number doctor. He drew a long breath – spasmodically – while his lips whispered: "God have mercy on me, a sinner." Dr. Callous then left his earthly pride, his machine medicine, his houses, his barns, his money behind him to appear, naked, before the Being he had flaunted.

Dr. Pressing bowed his head and said softly: "God have mercy on his soul."

He pulled the sheet over the face of the late Dr. Alexis Callous, took the weeping daughter by the hand and led her into another room followed by John. Kind neighbors came in to take charge of her. As the doctor and John walked slowly back to the Pressing office, the doctor said sadly: "What shall it profit a man if he gain the whole world and lose his own soul? I tell you, son, I do not believe that there is a man on earth who honestly in his heart is an Atheist. There is something in man that gives the lie to the pet theories of these young upstarts who go about braying, 'I am a scientist,' and who tear a passion to tatters in trying to explain the genesis of the universe, with their confounded, confusing talk about the atom being the basis of all things. That everything started by autogenesis. Why don't they tell us what started autogenesis? Who built the first atom?

"But it has always been so, my son, since the beginning of recorded history. The doctor of science bugaboo was first underwritten by Aristotle. His findings were accepted by this piece of chicanery called *pure science* for hundreds of years as the gospel truth. We know much of his work was a series of errors. Wise, or otherwise, doctors persecuted and attempted to burn Galileo at the stake. It took a century to prove that he was right. These are just a few of the myriads of cases in which doctors of one kind and another made grievous errors. The art of medicine has been no exception. I'll wager that the use of the jury mast, by one skilled in its use, would do more good than all the pharmaceuticals ever put out by companies specializing in handling, and man-handling, botanical drugs; in fact I see the tendency to get away from living drugs to the almost universal use of coal tar synthetics. This will be a curse to the people and upon medical doctors."

"I note you have a jury mast in the office," observed John. "I hope you will demonstrate its use to me. My reason is that I hear many of your patients state that they feel much better after a session with it."

"A most valuable modality, and I will demonstrate it to you at every opportunity. However, you will be leaving for Chicago in the morning to get caught up on *ju-jitsu* and *savate*. Make the very best use of your time. I need not tell you to watch your step. In fact you had better stay pretty close to Lavoisier and Kuwashimo, for they know their way around. There is also a Homeopath named Zollner with whom I hope you will meet and spend as much time as you can.

"I declare to you that Homeopathy has a lot of good points that we Allopaths should adopt and use. Zollner used to say that: 'If a Homeopath cannot help you, at least he will not harm you.' Of course many doctors make sport of the minute dosages administered by Homeopaths. Allopaths very often give too-high potency drugs and in too-high dosage. The human body is in a very fine state of equilibrium, and an overdose of drastic medicines may throw a man for a complete loss."

Dr. Pressing arose and drew a large medical book from the bookcase. He seated himself, and after flipping the pages for a few moments, read from a standard, medically acceptable book written by a great doctor, one John C. Gunn, M.D.

"'From the abuse of medicines, thousands and thousands die annually, without reflecting that they are taking poison. Unfortunately for mankind, yet most *fortunately for physicians,* the people cannot ascertain how many valuable lives are yearly destroyed by the constant dosing and drugging system.'

"If that does not prove that doctors kill as well as often bring about a cure, I do not know what does. But Dr. Gunn continues his condemnation of the A.M.A. type medicine by recounting the advent of a brand new doctor, who has been stuffed, like a Strassburg goose, with the idea that he can cure disease by over-drugging. It's as many famous doctors have so well stated: 'Nature heals and the doctor collects the fees.'

"Think of this example. Not far from where we live there is one of those pompous, brass-plated, recently graduated young doctors. What I am about to relate is rather common knowledge because an action in malpractice is pending. A farmer's wife made a visit at his office asking help for some obscure symptoms. The doctor made a diagnosis of anemia and malnutrition and wrote a prescription for Fowler's solution of potassium arsenite. Now Fowler's solution is a deadly poison unless given in minute doses. One usually prescribes 1 drop in water, thrice daily, the first day. Next day it is increased to 2 drops thrice daily, and so on until the patient is getting 8 to 10 drops, thrice daily. Then a short interim of no Fowler's solution. After this vacation the dosage drops back to 1 drop, thrice daily. Now, son, keep that dosage in mind while I tell you what that A.M.A. doctor did.

"The young idiot prescribed 1 teaspoonful three times a day, post cibum (after meals). The druggist, who really knew his toxicology, phoned him, calling attention to the toxic possibilities, and asked the doctor if this was not an error. The doctor – or was he a doctor? – was highly indignant and roared: 'Damn you, I never make mistakes. If you will not fill it as written, send the patient back to me and I will fix it for her. I have a bottle of Liquor potassii arsenitis (Author: Fowler's solution) in the office.'

He was so angry he forgot to demand the return of the prescription. The druggist locked it up in his safe. Well, the doctor did fix up Fowler's solution, prescribing the teaspoonful dosage as on his prescription.

"The woman died with acute arsenical poisoning on the fifth day. Just a plain case of medical manslaughter because of the miseducation of what might have been a promising young doctor. His career is ended before he has begun to live. He has no practice and, over his head like a sword of Damocles hangs a large damage suit. The thing will follow him the rest of his existence although the great A.M.A. apostle, Fishbein, will probably get him off the fish-hook. It would not surprise me if the young doctor took his own life, for I hear that his mental condition is something fearful."

"Well, I'll not use any Fowler's solution in my practice," said John.

Dr. Pressing replied: "If you do not, you will be eliminating one of our best remedies. Homeopaths get fine results with arsenicum album in anemia, certain nervous complaints, skin diseases that are hard to cure. Such chronic nervous diseases as disseminated sclerosis often yield to arsenic when carefully used and supervised by a physician who knows his materia medica. Combined with iron, it prevents bromism, while at the same time proving enormously valuable in anemia. There must have been quite a large number of similar *faux pas* on the part of A.M.A. doctors because that organization is making superhuman efforts to have it removed from the list of accepted remedies.

"And now, my boy, I want to talk to you about your trip to Chicago. That great city has been often called, 'The Syphlitic Sodom', and by others, who may have known through sad experiences, 'The Gonorrheal Gomorrah'. I found it far worse, morally and civically, than any spot in Europe.

"Let Chicago women alone. Of course there are countless fine, moral women there, but there is a tribe of loose, alimony-grasping Delilahs that would shame the very devil. They are always on the lookout for a good looking and well dressed young fellow like yourself. I know the president of the college where you are to take pre-med quite well. If it seems advisable, stay a week or so longer and I will fix it up with the college authorities. The roads are in fine shape now, so I will drive you to Chillocothe where you can get a very fast through train to Chicago. Let's go home and see what mother has for us."

* * *

The next morning early, after a motherly embrace from Mother Pressing the men started to Chillocothe. John caught his train there and landed in the windy city in mid-afternoon and went at once to a good hotel in the Loop. He called Lavoiser and Kuwashimo and made arrangements for the next day and the days following. Then he called a cab to take him to Dr. Zollner's office.

From the first hand clasp each man felt a magnetic attraction for the other. After mutual pleasantries had passed, Dr. Zollner said: "How I wish Dr. Pressing could have come with you. He writes me of the progress you have made even before you have attended medical school. You have been getting the healing art the right way, I assure you. Nothing like apprenticeship under a good man to set you on the road to success. By success I do not mean the sole accumulation of wealth by foul means such as fee splitting, unnecessary surgery done by poor surgeons, the actual tolling along of neurotics in order to get their money, and many other tricks perpetrated by many doctors right here in the home city of the American Medical Association.

"Now, John – I may call you John I trust – I have two patients due here any minute, and I want you to be present so you can get some idea of what is being done with Homeopathy." While Dr. Zollner yet spoke his office door was heard to open and close. The doctor opened his private office door and invited the patient to enter. He introduced John to him as a colleague and asked the patient to explain what had been done for him.

The patient was a man of about forty years; tall, lean, muscular and with the hallmark of intelligence in his eyes. He was evidently a man of education for he addressed John in perfect English: "I will be glad to do so. I am a high school principal. I have always had good health until a little over two years ago. Then some nervous condition would not let me sleep. Just as I was about to drop asleep, the muscles in several parts of my body would give an extreme jerk.

"Rarely did I get sleep until 3 A.M. and I was just worn out all the time. I consulted several Allopathic doctors and they gave me all sorts of medicine that made me feel even worse. Great blotches broke out on my face, especially on the forehead. Some people thought I had syphilis and avoided me. After taking various medicines from four doctors, one after another, I was advised by a friend to see Dr. Zollner. He gave me some small tablets which I was to take, one or more half an hour before retiring. Now I sleep like a baby. No more of that fearful jerking. I feel fine. Doctor Zollner, I am about out of the tablets. Will I need to continue taking them?"

"Possibly I had better give you a few more, but do not take them unless needed. That is, if the jerking returns, then take one tablet. Goodbye, Frank."

Frank must have passed the next patient on the way up because the second man walked into the outer office at once.

In the private office Dr. Zollner asked him: "Did that liquid stop the severe pain?"

"Yes, thank heaven and you, Doctor, the pain and spasm disappeared in ten hours after you brought me that medicine."

"Have you noticed any blood in the urine since then?"

"Not a bit," declared the patient. "This really is something when that medicine you gave me looked and tasted like common water."

"Tell my colleague here, how many doctors you went to and what they said," requested Dr. Zollner.

"I went to three doctors of medicine and all three made a different diagnosis and gave me a different kind of medicine. Not all at once, you understand, but after each man, in his turn, had failed. I went to a fourth and he advised me to go to a specialist – one interview cost me $25.00. He wanted me to enter a hospital. All those three weeks I was going through hell. Had to take dope to get a wink of sleep. Luckily I encountered an old friend who had had some similar experiences and he advised me to come to you, Dr. Zollner. Doctor, if medicine is a science, why couldn't four men agree on a diagnosis and treatment?"

The patient left the office after paying a very moderate fee of $3.00 for consultation and a four-ounce bottle of medicine. John took out his notebook and asked Dr. Zollner what magic medicine he used in these two cases. The doctor grinned and replied: "Do not laugh, John, for the first patient got nothing but a few tablets of a high attenuation of ignatia amara. It is most valuable in many nervous derangements, a cure for the tobacco habit, and of great aid in patients suffering from excessive grief. Be sure and get acquainted with this natural curative agent. Study it thoroughly. Use it. The second patient got a highly attenuated solution of cantharides."

John interrupted the doctor. "Cantharides! I have read that that is one of the greatest irritants to mucous membranes existing."

"That is right, John, but regardless of what any physician will tell you, Homeopathy cures and our medicines never kill. You see, Dr. Hanneman discovered by actual tests that *Similia Similibus Curantur.* You understand? In short, if a certain dose of a certain drug, or even food gives certain symptoms, a greatly attenuated dose of the same substance will relieve the condition.

"Homeopaths are great believers in the *Vis Naturae Medicatrix.* That is, the natural healing power of nature. If one cannot regenerate and stimulate that natural fighting power of the body, that patient is pretty likely to die. Every Homeopathic remedy has been tested and proved tens or thousands of times. The patient who just left was given saw palmetto, sandal wood, couch grass, abies hexamin and heaven knows what else. He became worse because those drugs were not indicated. His symptoms were exactly those that he would have had if he had been poisoned with cantharides – intolerable urging to urinate constantly with awful pain and spasms in the urethra. The urine came only in drops, then the urine was flecked with blood. This was a typical cantharides case – and he got highly attenuated cantharides, with the result that he called me up four hours after he had taken the first dose and told me he was much easier.

"And remember, John, all this happened after four Allopaths and a specialist in urology could not help him. Regardless of what medical course you pursue, do not sell Homeopathic remedies short. I have a long list of cures by Homeopathy after Allopathy had failed. Well, you will want to be getting back to your hotel and settled for the night. You will probably have a rough, tiring time tomorrow with your *ju-jitsu.*"

* * *

John arose betimes the next morning and after a shower, a clean shave and a good breakfast, walked to the studio of Mr. Kuwashimo and presented the letter which Dr. Pressing had written to that worthy. After the wondrous reports about that Japanese science, John was rather taken aback as he eyed the rather diminutive specimen, while the specimen conned the letter of introduction. But when he reached out his right hand for a shake, and felt like he had got his hand caught in a cement mill, he began revising his opinion. Kuwashimo was a handsome little Jap, not an inch over 5 feet 4 inches. He spoke with a decided lisp, and smiled and bowed from the waist as if he was hinged at the navel. His age? He appeared to be timeless for quite a number of years ago he had taught Dr. Pressing the real art of self defense, without guns, knives, canes, or loss of blood.

"So very glad to meet you," he lisped. "Will you honor me by entering my poor studio? You will want to go right to work, so please go into that alcove and undress. Then put on these clothes – they are freshly laundered, sterilized and will fit you quite well."

John did as directed. The uniform, or whatever one might call it, was two pieces, a sort of heavy jacket of cotton material, and as for pants, they approximated the modern shorts, also made of coarse, strong cotton. On reentering the other room John noted that there was a heavy quilted mat on the floor. Kuwashimo directed him to be seated on the sidelines while he gave a lesson to a police sergeant, a burly man who must have weighed at least 80 pounds more than the Japanese.

The Jap manhandled the burly cop and mopped the floor with him, to John's absolute bewilderment. He noted, too, that the Jap had a knowledge of nerve centers that was almost fantastic. He knew when and where to shoot out a hand and grip the policeman in spots that made him yell 'Uncle'. But the cop was there for that purpose, to learn how to catch and subdue criminals and the insane, not to mention his personal defense under tricky circumstances. And this cop could surely take it. John noted that the two wrestlers faced each other and then reached out and took a firm hold on each other's jacket lapel. It was so easy, it seemed, to turn one's back to the other and then, without letting go, bend quickly over and toss the opponent completely over to land on his head, provided, that is, that the tossee did not know what to do about it.

"Now. I show you how to make man unconscious without drawing blood. You just strike him here on the neck under the ear, with the edge of the open hand. But be very easy for it easy to break neck if too hard the blow," said Kuwo. He easily avoided the cop's grasp and demonstrated by striking a light blow at the designated spot. The cop roared with pain, which quickly subsided.

"Good Lord, that is terrific," he said. "Now show me more methods of quieting a prisoner."

Kuwo said: "Hold the hand open, bending slightly backward. I show you, like this. I simply use the base of the hand instead of a fist – so."

Again the cop cried out in pain and his eyes became glazed. By this time the officer was sweating like rain and he panted for air.

The Jap was cool, calm, smiling. "You must never lose the temper," he said. "Just a moment of anger and any *ju-jitsu* man can put you out circulation. One more thing and you have had enough for today. Now suppose you face me and try to choke me with both hands. I simply place my hands palm to palm, make wedge so, thrust them up between your wrists and spread my hands and break your hold. If it was a serious matter, I could now kick you on the patella, or knee pan with my right toe, following quickly by kicking you between the thighs with my right toe. That would double you up and then I would jerk up either knee and strike you in the face."

The cop grinned and said: "I'll take your word for that. You need not demonstrate. Here is the pay for today's lesson. See you Saturday, same time."

"Well, Mr. Pressing, your name John, the letter say. May I call you John?" John was perfectly agreeable. Kuwo proceeded. "Now, John, grasp my lapel as other man did. I grasp yours like so. Now you turn quick, throw your body forward, throw me over your head."

"I might hurt you," protested John.

"No, John, no hurt. You throw now, hard. Try throw me so my head hit floor."

John did his best and over his head flew the Jap, rather doubling up while he was in the air, appearing to be like a rocking chair rocker. He turned clear over and rolled to his two feet.

"You see how easy?" said Kuwo. "Now is show how do. Stand here, bend body at middle, put head between legs and fall forward. Not be afraid, simply cannot hurt."

To his great surprise and delight, John did a very creditable job after a few trials.

"Now watch backfall," said Kuwo. He fell backward, bending at the middle as he fell, and rolled up like a rocking chair.

After much coaching and some slight bumps on his south end, John found the secret and did very well.

"Now, John, learn when fall to slap mat, like so. That save from hard fall that break bones." John caught the rudiments of 'mat slapping' after a few trials. Kuwo smiled broadly in approval. "Good. You learn quick. That enough for one day. We drink cup tea, no?"

While they drank several cups of the most delicious tea that John had ever tasted, Kuwo said: "Doctor Pressing say you going to be doctor. Yes? Every doctor should know. I show you how put my deep sleep press here." Suiting the action to the word, he reached over and pressed gently on a spot in John's neck. There was no pain, but he felt himself slipping toward unconsciousness. Kuwo loosed his slight grip and the feeling left John.

"You see how easy when know *ju-jitsu*? Easy kill enemy that try tricks. Come tomorrow at same time. Now time you eat lunch and go see Mr. Lavoisier. Very good man. *Savate* and *lecan* both very good defend self. Goodbye. I see you tomorrow, yes?"

John walked down Wabash a few blocks and entered a nice cafeteria and ate a light, but nourishing meal, then to Lavoisier on Boul Miche. After half an hour of *savate* and *escrime,* he was rather tired and went to his hotel to rest and clean up for what home folks call supper.

He was surprised on awakening next morning to find he was only moderately stiff and sore. He ate a good breakfast and then back to Kuwo's studio. Kuwo rapidly massaged the sore spots with some kind of Japanese unguent and they went at it again. John perfected his falling tactics, his mat slapping, and the flying eagle as per the Japanese version. Kuwo next showed him the Malay grip, and demonstrated the exact spot in the neck where an attacker could be put *hors du combat* in a second.

That afternoon he had another session with Lavoisier and found that some of the methods the French used in defense ran parallel to the Jap version. He reasoned that the French had borrowed from the Land of the Rising Sun.

While they were at it, the champion French rapier artist happened in and John got a real idea of what duelling meant. Although the two Frenchmen were fixed friends, nevertheless, while they fenced, they glared into each other's eyes like wild beasts. (Author: we note this same thing among football players these days. Probably Nero's gladiators did likewise. I watched soldiers at bayonet practice in World War I and they cursed and swore and plunged at the dummies, trained to hate and kill a man who never harmed them, without mercy. When will so-called civilized men learn that when God said: "Thou shalt not kill," he meant THOU SHALT NOT KILL. Failure to obey that important commandment engenders universal hate. Hate is the antithesis of love. GOD IS LOVE, and as long as men hate, one need not die to know hell.)

That night John wrote his folks a long letter describing his experiences and started to walk to the old Post Office at Dearborn, Clark, Monroe and Jackson. As he was turning into the Clark Street entrance three young ruffians tried to rough him, the object robbery no doubt, perhaps worse. The largest of the rowdies, about 20 years old, threw a "haymaker" at John's head. Remembering the Jap flying eagle, John caught the thug's right wrist with both hands, pulled the thug closer until his armpit was over John's shoulder. With little effort, John pitched the attacker over on his head – and to unconsciousness. This was done so quickly that the thug's companions were unable to help. When they saw their strongest man lying in gentle sleep on the granite steps, they took off south on Clark.

A crowd began gathering and a policeman rushed up shouting: "What's going on here?" He glanced at the fallen man and then at John. It was the Sergeant of Police that John had seen at Kuwo's the previous day. (Who says that truth is not stranger than fiction?) "Begorra, you are the lucky one. This rat is wanted on a dozen counts for strong-arming citizens, rape and attempted manslaughter. We've been combing the town for him for weeks. And here you come in from the sticks and get him cold."

"Will I be held as a witness?" asked John.

"Not unless you want to claim the reward for his capture. We have enough on him without your testimony to send him to Joliet for life."

Another policeman came up and the Sergeant turned the ruffian over to the patrolman and walked John to his hotel. As they walked along, the Sergeant said: "Son, this is one tough town. Let me urge you not to walk these darker streets at night time, yes, any time. Some of these rats will kill a man for the price of a drink at Hinky Dink's dump. And say, we can both swear that *ju-jitsu* pays off, eh lad? Will I be seeing you at Kuwo's studio on Saturday?"

"You sure will if I'm still living," replied John.

"Son," said the Police Sergeant, "I have a boy about your age and he has gone cracked about women. Let me urge you not to have anything to do with any woman you are likely to meet while you are in Chicago. Venereal diseases are real hell up here. See you Saturday."

John was invited to Dr. Zollner's home out on Washington Boulevard for a genuine German Sunday dinner. This gave John many hours to discuss medicine and surgery with a very successful and human doctor, a real *rara avis* in the hindquarters town that housed the unconscionable medical monopoly.

After a marvelous dinner of *hassenpfeffer* and all the trimmings, Dr. Zollner asked: "John, I have three calls to make. How would you like to accompany me?"

"With all my heart," said John.

The two entered the doctor's old Ford and drove over to one of Chicago's slums off Roosevelt Road. The car stopped at a miserable, unpainted two-story house and the two men entered and climbed up a rickety stair that seems to be always on the point of falling. Dr. Zollner led the way along a dark hall that was lined on either side by garbage cans, coal scuttles and all sorts of other rubbish. As they neared the last door the sound of someone with a dreadful soft cough, mingled with gagging was plainly heard.

"A terminal case of miliary TB," whispered the doctor. They entered the dismal room and saw a young woman, perhaps 28 years old, propped up in a dirty bed. She held a spit cup in her right hand and occasionally used it sickeningly, at least it seemed so to John. Dr. Zollner did all that he possibly could: took her temperature, felt her pulse, listened to her chest with his stethoscope, ordered the attendant, her mother, to give the medicine, and the food as prescribed, said he'd be back the next day about one, and left with John.

"Any hope for the girl?" asked John.

"No. Absolutely no hope," replied the doctor.

"Doctor, is TB strictly a germ disease?"

"No, John, TB is almost 100% caused by poverty which presupposes poor living quarters, poor or little food, and, probably a predisposition to the disease, or, perhaps, a lowered *vis naturae medicatrix*. In time to come it will be found that TB is founded on starvation; that is, too little of certain foods, and too little sunlight. It has been proved in the Alps Mountains by Bernhardt and Rollier that most cases of TB can be cured by sunlight plus decently selected food. Niels Finsen of Denmark has been getting excellent results by combining sunlight, or artificial sunlight, with clean air and good, not necessarily expensive foods, and has brought about remissions in thousands of cases. Yes, my boy, TB will be conquered when humans are able to live normal lives, that is eat good food, get proper rest, get out in the sunlight."

John then said: "I read someplace that men who work in lime quarries, in the sunlight, never get TB. Is that statement true?"

"Yes, I believe it is because the limestone is mostly calcium. The powdered calcium-bearing limestone enters the body through the lungs. I know there is some property in sunshine that fixes the TB germs by a calcium incapsulation of the bacteria. Yes, decent living conditions and food will usually prevent TB."

(Author: this prediction made some twenty five years ago has been absolutely proved factual. Morris Fishbein, who claims to be a physician, altho he said under oath that he had never had a patient, and who was made the goat by the A.M.A. because, for some reason, he began telling the truth, collected and collated a great quantity of medical findings made by undeniably good doctors, and published a book that furnishes us with ample proof of the soundness of Dr. Zollner's quarter-century-old prediction. Fishbein's book states that:

Tuberculosis is largely a disease of poverty and malnutrition. (See Fishbein's Modern Medical Adviser, page 257). The same book states, and that portion is the absolute truth, that TB is a social disease because it spreads where there is poverty, malnutrition, overcrowding, bad housing and exposure to the elements. Fishbein's book also states, and states truly, that Negroes in the crowded districts in northern cities have the highest death rate of any group in the community. And that Chicago Mexicans had eleven times the average rate of the rest of the people of Chicago.

(Author: a short time ago, a man calling himself a Christian, Benson his name, called for suggestions to put crops now rotting in warehouses and caves to humanitarian uses. Your author suggested that a large portion now being given to foreign despotisms might well be used to feed hungry Americans, now and forever threatened by TB through malnutrition. The Secretary of Agriculture wrote me a personal letter – yet did nothing but bat his assistants over the habitable globe trying to force our enemies and false friends to accept our surpluses – FOR NOTHING.

Taking the known facts that there would never be a surplus if every American had decent food, housing, clothing, your author went through Representative Smith (Rep. Wis.) and got the most horrifying data from the Census Bureau that nearly 6 million families – get that, families, not individuals – have gross annual incomes of less than one thousand dollars. And nearly four million families have gross annual incomes of less than five hundred dollars.

Furthermore, while millions suffer from lack of doctors, nurses and hospitals, Uncle Simple taxes our shirts off to send them to our false friends. Added to this there are at present eighty-one different organizations seeking, demanding, threatening us out of billions of dollars. The organizers of these alleged charitable groups are actually robbing us out of our money, given out of the goodness of our hearts, and the same groups do not give an accounting of the billions collected. As for instance, pay of officers, etc.

Let us repeat a quatrain from our beloved Longfellow:

Were half the power that fills the world with terror,

Were half the wealth bestowed on camps and courts,
Given to redeem the human from error,
There were no need of arsenals or forts."

Camps and courts? We today are supporting the greatest despotisms known to History's blood-soaked pages. Will we never realize that, in spite of our grand give-aways, we are the world's most hated and despised people? We are loading debts on the necks of our descendents that they will be paying off for the next millenium. Do we realize what Russia, France, Britain, Syria, Israel, India, etc., ad infinitum, owe us and at the same time placard their cities with, YANKS GO HOME? We Americans surely are gluttons for punishment! Think again that official government figures show, as stated supra, nearly six million families with less than $1000.00 a year income! Why don't we concern ourselves with *them?*)

When Dr. Zollner and John, the future Dr. Pressing, had reached another ramshackle, falling-down two-story building a few doors down the street, they again mounted a stairs that swayed under their weight. The door to an upstairs apartment led to one room without toilet or bath. The only heating element was a cracked, ancient cook stove of the vintage of 1890. They were greeted by a pleasant-faced woman of about forty.

"How is Mary?" inquired Dr. Zollner.

"Not much change as far as I can see. She is still carrying a temperature and is delirious at times." This lady was the patient's elder sister. The patient was 28 years of age.

She lay there softly moaning and picking at her covers with her fingers, a serious symptom called carphology. The sister then excused herself, the cause probably being that she had to search some toilet facilities. After she left, Dr. Zollner quickly checked her pulse, respiration and listened to her chest with his stethoscope. Then he briefed John on the case to date.

"John, this is another one of those cases of incorrect diagnosis, unneeded surgery done by a young self-elected surgeon, and at gougery prices. For the record, it was done strictly for the doctor's own pocketbook. This young and daring Allopath, a member of the medical monopoly, called for a certain, but obscure, syndrome, found that this girl's family had saved a few hundred dollars and persuaded them to have the girl operated."

"What was she operated for? What was the diagnosis?" asked John.

Dr. Zollner replied: "The doctor threw a lot of long, septuapedalion names at them and urged an exploratory laparotomy to find what ailed her. The fact is, the doctor didn't know, or perhaps care, for he hired another surgeon to open her belly – a surgeon who took the young doctor's word for everything. The operation was performed. No pathology was discovered, although they cut her abdomen into shreds. Then they did a poor job of repair work and walked out on her because the family could not raise another $250.00.

"Friends took up the matter with the Board of Health (A.M.A. ruled) and the Chicago Medical Society (a branch of A.M.A.), without any punitive action on the part of either of them. That, John, is the rule right here in the very bastion of A.M.A. politics. In any event, one of the girl's friends called me in and I found that, despite all the Oriental harem hospitalization where all go around draped like Scherezade, the trauma was infected. She has shown some improvement and I believe we can pull her through without further packing-house surgery. Homeopaths have agents that increase the natural resistance of the human body to infection. Take out your note book and write down echinacea and calcium sulfid. Make a thorough study at your leisure."

(Author: You are seeking the truth. As a postscript to this chapter, you will get the Positive, The Most Damnable Facts About Medical Racketeering, Chicanery, Manslaughter and Murder Ever Known In The World's History.

There *IS* A Cancer Cure That Cures.

The A.M.A. Knows *At Least Three* Of Them.

The A.M.A. and the F.D.A., its bureaucratic slave, seek to prevent these cures from being known and used to save millions of lives. Senator Tobey's son was sent home to die of cancer by A.M.A. doctors. A 'quack' saved the boy's life. As a result Senator Tobey started a Senate investigation. The main investigator, a fearless Irishman who feared neither A.M.A. nor the A.M.A. master, Beelzebub, investigated and found and condemned the following crimes and misdemeanors committed by the two organizations. Here is a portion of FitzGerald's report to the Senate Committee to investigate cancer cures, and to record the malignancy and inhumanity of A.M.A. and their paid stooges in the government whom all of us supports.

1. FitzGerald said: "There is reason to believe the A.M.A. has been hasty, capricious, arbitrary, and downright dishonest. The alleged machinations of Dr. J. J. Moore (for the past ten years treasurer of the A.M.A.) could involve the A.M.A. and others in an interstate conspiracy of alarming proportions. (The others spoken of can hardly refer to any other than Senator Bricker known by wise men as, The Bricker, (Rep. Ohio), and to the Food and Drug Administration, and possibly the Agriculture Department).

2. *"Dr. Moore's rascality."* (Moore was treasurer of A.M.A. and still is. The top brass cannot kick him out as it did Fishbein.)

3. FitzGerald said: "Behind and over all this is the weirdest conglomeration of corrupt motives, intrigue, selfishness, jealousy, obstruction and conspiracy I have ever seen." (FitzGerald is still speaking about the A.M.A., the Federal Drug & Food Administration, the great American Free Press – free to malign, persecute, torment, calumniate, villify those who have no means of redress.)

4. FitzGerald then gives names, addresses and other data

of many cancer patients, all types, all sent home to die by A.M.A. doctors, and who then got back their health under the Hoxsey treatment and other treatments. (Are there five or more in your family? Did you know that one or more of that family will die of cancer? Wake up and write your congressmen demanding that the case against A.M.A. and F.D.A. be reopened. Wake up! Wake up! Wake up! Or die the cancer death!)

5. And FitzGerald said: "How long is the American people going to stand for this?" Well, how long are you going to stand for this brutal, blood-stained conduct on the part of those you pay most handsomely to protect your health and heal your diseases? The U.S. Mails are wide open. Write your Congressmen and Senators and demand the facts, as provided in the Constitution of the United States. Then, and only then will you get that redress guaranteed to all of us by the Constitution. Understand, every one of you who read this, that I am trying to save your lives and the lives of those that are bound to you by mutual love. I wish I could meet every reader face to face and see if I could not get you boiling mad. Haven't we one bit of the guts that our Colonial forefathers had? We fuss and shed crocodile tears about the Hungarian massacre. Have you never read of the didoes done by Hungarian soldiers when they had the upper hand? Dry your tears about despotisms in other parts of the world and try to help to save *all* humanity by peaceful means, by voting right, by petitioning Congress for redress from the rascality of those in high spots in government, by voting for principle, not for party. A senator recently said: "Nine tenths of the American people have to be fools so the other tenth can be elected to rule them!"

FitzGerald reported word for word the sage advice of many of the world's leading doctors who damn the use of surgery, X-rays and radium in treating cancer. Yet, the U.S. Food and Drug Administration had lying placards posted in every post office warning that Hoxsey was a quack, and that surgery, radium and X-rays were the *only* hope for cancer cure. Liars!

Why didn't the A.M.A. approved methods cure Taft, Vandenberg, Babe Zaharias, and millions more who died under A.M.A. approved mistreatment? FitzGerald reported all types of cancer cured with Hoxsey and other treatments that the A.M.A. calls quack remedies.

Many times, in my magazine articles I have told you where to write and get the documented facts about medical rascality, poisons (many of them in everything you eat and drink) and all of the poisons and cancer producers. Won't you let me help save you? Or are you worth saving? You should know best.

Now let's talk about sadistic surgery. Documented brutal, heartrending, bestial, unneeded surgery – facts well known to every health agency in the U.S. Government. In fact, the head of the Public Health organization recently said: "Many doctors are no better than plumbers." The doctor-to-be Dr. John Marsh Pressing will hear much about the rascality in medicine and government before he is ready to hang out his shingle. But you are getting a good preview.

Note: Every statement is fully documented and the documents are ready for inspection at any time.

If your Congressmen write you denying any statement made herein, you can put them down as prevaricators.

CHAPTER 7

"I WENT INTO SURGERY BECAUSE I FOUND I COULD MAKE MORE MONEY IN TWO HOURS THAN A G.P. (family doctor) COULD MAKE IN A WEEK OR MORE." – Statement made by a prominent surgeon in a medical meeting at Kansas City, Missouri.

A recent issue of the *Chicago Tribune* disclosed a case of a man who had a gut operation. He was sewed up and it was called a successful operation. He complained of awful pain and several days later he was again opened up. A pair of 5 inch forceps were found and removed. The man died. Medical men were able to get this crime quashed. No punitive action by the State Board or A.M.A.

Recently in a Chicago hospital a man's diseased right leg was to be amputated. He woke up to find that A.M.A. surgeons had amputated the *wrong* leg. Back he went to have the diseased *right* leg removed. Are you ready for the $64,000 surgery where they may take off your head in operating on an indicated removal of an infected toenail?

Not long ago a physician advised his patient, a perfectly healthy man, to have his tonsils removed. The operation was a success. The patient choked to death and a post mortem showed a large gauze sponge was left in the throat and was drawn down into the lungs. A biopsy (microscopic examination) of the tonsils showed them absolutely healthy. No punitive action by A.M.A.

A U.S. Army doctor told a Captain he had a cancer and that his only hope lay in immediate surgery. The X-ray pictures showed, nay proved, that he had a cancer, a carcinoma. It was discovered just in the nick of time that the supposed cancer was nothing but a thumb smudge on the film.

Dr. Paul R. Hawley – he is a very high class physician and surgeon – wrote: "Far too many operations are being performed. These unneeded operations are just plain dishonest, money making, and I can prove it."

After a fifteen-year-long survey of appendix removals at the St. Joseph Mercy Hospital, Ann Arbor, Michigan, the center of the medical school of Michigan University, on actual examinations of the removed suspected appendices, it was proved that more than one out of every five removed were healthy. In many hospitals it has been found that at least 60% of all appendectomies are not indicated.

There was Dr. H. L. Foss, one of the best surgeons in America, who recently spoke before a medical convention, saying that tens of thousands of unnecessary surgical operations were being done every year, worse yet, performed by men only one in twenty of whom was capable of doing surgery. That, he said, was the reason that this country had the highest post operative death rate in the world. Dr. A. D. Campbell, a gynecologist and surgeon, McGill University, condemned most vigorously the American medical doctors who rushed women to the operating table without a proper diagnosis; and after being overtreated with far too much, over-advertised vitamins, and other pharmaceutical makers' concoctions.

The chicanery of the medical profession in New York City was so outrageous and criminal that Governor Thomas Dewey appointed the Morland Committee to investigate the malodorous condition. The committee reported that they had discovered that over 3000 medical doctors in that area demanded and accepted kickbacks from surgeons, specimen laboratories, medical book publishers, makers of surgical instruments, pharmaceutical houses, serum and vaccine factories, druggists, opticians, in fact every business even remotely connected to the medical doctors.

One surgeon remarked satirically: "Hell's bells, the next thing these *fellows will demand is kickbacks from morticians.* I shouldn't wonder if they were not doing it already when I read the medical journals."

In addition most of these ghouls were advising unnecessary surgery and gougery prices so the surgeon had to charge all the traffic would bear. These same ghouls were unquestionably guilty of diagnosing a simple chest cold as pneumonia, and shooting the victim full of penicillin, which 'blunder' drug is supposed to have killed more than it has cured. Thousands of so-called cures brought about by penicillin and other products of putrefaction, *were not correctly diagnosed in the first place.* Rest in bed, careful diet did the job. As Franklin said: "God heals the patient. The doctor collects the fee."

These things of horror and fair robbery will be more and more known to the future honest doctor, John Marsh Pressing. We left John in Chicago as he made calls with a Homeopathic doctor, Dr. Zollner. May we return to their company as they went went about, like Jesus, doing good?

* * *

The next patient to see was but a few doors away. The patient proved to be a little girl of about seven, another victim of brutal organized medicine. She had been subjected to a tonsil operation that, according to Dr. Zollner, she had not needed. But some rapacious young doctor fresh from his internship, and ravenous for a paying patient, had taken one glance into her throat and declared she must have her tonsils removed at once, or he would not be held responsible for the child's future. No attempt had been made by the budding young physician to dissect out the tonsils. He had evidently used a Sleuter-Ballinger tonsilotomy and gouged out a considerable amount of the healthy tissues, and then had not gotten the whole tonsils.

The patient was removed to her home after a night of hell and hemorrhaging in the hospital. She began to hemorrhage badly on the following night, and as the brilliant neophyte surgeon could not be found, Dr. Zollner had been called in on emergency. (Note: the young doctor had left his practice and gone on a fishing trip in Wisconsin.) Dr. Zollner had succeeded in stopping the bleeding by packing the cavity with gauze, wet with Monsell's solution. This was his second trip and, fortunately, the wound had begun to heal.

He remarked to John: "This is just luck and *vis naturae medicatrix,* not medical science. This young squirt should have his license to practice revoked, but it will not be, because he is a relative of Bundensen, who is Czar over the Chicago Health Department. I don't know when, but sometime, someplace, this person will get repaid with interest.

"John, let me make a prediction and a warning. Today over half of tonsillectomies are not indicated. The tonsils were put there for a purpose by Almighty God. In days to come tonsillectomies done as routine will be considered in the same category as cannibalism. You will live to see that time, mark my words."

"What do you consider the true function of tonsils?" asked John.

"From many years' observation I am positive that they serve as filters to withhold germs from entering and finding lodgement in the blood stream. I think another function is that the tonsils manufacture antibodies against invading bacteria. I know many doctors who agree with me that the removal of these glands to prevent colds is pure bosh. I know that pneumonias strike children who have this operation, more than those who still retain the tonsils. John, much of surgery is nothing but greed for wealth, and sadism."

(Author: How right Dr. Zollner was. We note that recently at an A.M.A. meeting, Dr. R. G. Sproul stated that many doctors were little better than plumbers. Dr. Sproul is a fairly honest doctor with unquestioned ability and medical acumen. At the same convention, Dean Justin of Duke University, an A-grade school said that shysters and scalawags seek admission to medical schools for the sole purpose, as one of them testified under oath, "to make a lot of jack quick." How many of us would like to have his name so he could be called in an emergency? Fellow sufferers shut off that TV or radio long enough to write your Congressmen in Washington and demand, for that is your constitutional right, that they go to work representing us, the people. To open up the FitzGerald findings. Demand that the A.M.A. be investigated.

Demand that Congress open up the investigation started by Senator Tobey – A thorough investigation of medical monopoly, as well as the food and drug people. Find why they blackmail Dr. Harry Hoxsey just because he is curing cancer after orthodox medics flop.

About the criminal slaughters of the tonsils: all documented records! Hundreds of honest doctors and surgeons are now on record in stating that: "Tonsils and adenoids are not useless appendages to the human throat, but serve the very useful purpose of excluding germs, as well as dust and dirt from the lungs, not to mention from the life of man, his blood, for as stated the Bible, 'The blood is the life.' (This is an exact quote made by America's most reputable throat and nose specialist.)

A group of German investigators on glands and glandular secretions (endocrinologists), after long research, made the categorical statement that tonsils are factories for antibodies. against invading disease germs. Very significantly, the journal of the A.M.A. warned rash, impecunious fee-splitting doctors that tonsil operations should be strictly avoided in a polio season. It also warned against the promiscuous use of vaccines during the polio season. As of this date, November 13th, 1957, there is a mighty fight raging behind the A.M.A. walls between the A.M.A. and Herman Bundensen, czar with the prerogative of life and death over Chicago's millions. The A.M.A. protests Bundensen's pus-shooting with three vaccines at one and the same time. In this particular case, we must in common decency state that, for some unknown resason the A.M.A. is correct in its assumption that this technique is fearfully dangerous. The medical societies, by the laws of averages, had to be right once in a million times. Nevertheless, nothing can wash away the A.M.A. crime of preventing known cancer cures to continue to cure after A.M.A. sychophants have sent the patient home to die!

Dr. Albert Kaiser, a highly reputable and apparently honest throat specialist reported that he had made a study of one thousand children. Half had had tonsillectomies. The other 500 did not have their tonsils torn out. This study was carried on over ten years. He stated that the incidence of colds, ear troubles and croup were equal in both groups. And Dr. Kaiser stated categorically, "There is a higher incidence of bronchitis and pneumonia in those who have had their tonsils removed." A.M.A. and F.D.A. please take note and try to obtain a little more selflessness and humanity into your hard shells. Dr. Burnett, another highly reputable physician and surgeon pointed out most definitely that there seemed to be a direct relation between the pus-punching of our children and the polio epidemics. The author has a personal letter, and you can bet it is in a safe place, from an internationally respected board of health executive. The doctor stated that the recent epidemic of polio in Chicago immediately followed the administration of small pox, Schick and Salk vaccine. He states that there were so many cases following the first injections of Salk vaccine, directly attributable to the fact that the monkey-kidney stew had not had the virus sufficiently attenuated.

Then he said: "From some tests we have been making, we are sure that what is now called Salk vaccine is nothing but sterile water. Or else the stuff is water containing the supposed virus causing polio, so sterlized that it contains nothing that can help or harm. We seem to recall the fact that the fearful disease attacking the world about 1919 was called Spanish Flu. No specific vaccine was produced and anybody who says otherwise is a liar. Nevertheless Spanish Flu died out by itself. Polio ditto if we stop these insecticides.

"I tell you W.C. all this rot about a vaccine for this new type of the common cold is one of the worst kinds of medical and serological chicanery that has appeared in our generation. It will make hundreds of millions for Merck, Parke Davis, Lilly *et al.* And the sad part is that the owners of the A.M.A. know this and take the blood-stained thirty pieces of silver."

This physician is still a member of the A.M.A. because he has to be until some modern David shall arise and smite the anthropophagus beast, the present medical monopoly, leaving its ever-putrid cadaver to further pollute the air until eaten by scavenger buzzards, leaving the whitening skeleton as a perpetual memorial to learned quackery, chicanery and charlatanism. Thus, freed from its fetid fetters, the Art of Healing can again take its rightful place as the right hand of God. And not before. The author spent nearly thirty-five years as representative of pharmaceutical houses, surgical instrument makers and manufacturers of physical therapy apparatus, and has personally observed some of the most ignorant, the most brutal, and of necessity the least friendly to God, acts done by doctors of medicine, whose great desire was to get the money and get it regardless of their Hippocratic Oaths and the commands of Deity. And every one a member of the A.M.A.

And on the contrary, thank God, the author has seen Doctors of Medicine performing acts of mercy and human brotherhood that certainly will receive those golden words of commendation: "Come ye blessed of my Father . . . Inasmuch as you did it unto one of the least of these, ye did it unto me." Thank God for that kind of doctors regardless of their particular school or methods just as long as they assuage pain and heal the sick. The justly celebrated Dr. Archambault once wrote, and the author has the record: "A diseased crypt in a tonsil no more justifies a tonsillectomy than does a sore big toenail justify an amputation of the leg at the hip." Furthermore, he called attention to the enormous blood supply in the tonsils signifying that the intact tonsils are of peculiar value in the growth and development through the possible endocrine secretions.

Dr. Harry Hawkin is another highly reputable doctor of medicine who points out the dangers inherent in many doctors' belief that a tonsillectomy is a simple operation. Far too often, he said, a tonsillectomy brings on serious complications such as death from hemorrhage, abcesses and pneumonia. The American Child Health Association made a thorough study of a selected group of 1000 children, employing a group of supposedly reputable, trustworthy medical doctors. The report issued by this group was absolutely fantastic. It simply demonstrated that there was such a divergence of opinions and advice that the work might just as well have been undertaken by the Jolly Order of Morticians. It amply proved that over half of the so-called Eye, Ear, Nose and Throat specalists didn't know their southwest exposure from the Mount Lassen crater when the matter of tonsils came up.

These are but a few of the hundreds of documented records your author has to place on evidence when the proper time arrives. My home has been burglarized of documents. My home and four laboratories were set on fire, after being burglarized. Those crimes can only be attributed to high officals in the *American Medical Association and the Wisconsin Alumni Research Foundation*. When the proper time arrives, and I feel it is soon, the American public is going to be treated to a record of malignant conspiracies existing in State, Government and medical politics that would make Joe Stalin seem an angel of peace and light. And these conspiracies have to do with your life, the lives of those you love, with the very existence of the United States. We lately cursed the givers and receivers of deep freezers, furs, cars, perfumes. We let politicians pull the wool over our eyes. Without thought of principle, we elected another gang of political amateurs and grafters. If we have read the papers we know that the same situation obtains — crooks in the F.D.A. and in the A.M.A. dominate every second of our lives.

By now don't you know that cigarettes cause cancer, heart diseases, and high blood pressure that today holds over 30 million Americans in constant jeopardy of strokes? Don't you know that probably every thing you eat, drink, the very air you breathe is laden with poisons? Do you believe the lying figures put out by many government departments that we overpay while their heads take plane trips all over the globe with their families and friends, while we pay through the nose? During 1957, more than a hundred Congressmen and their aides flew all over the earth and took their families along. Did you know that Senators get free barber services? Did you know that government personnel get free hospital and medical care while we pay and shout hurrah?

Didn't you know, or do you care a continental, that villainous Congressmen, guilty of selling us down the river, drew lush pensions while they were in durance vile? Did you know that Congressional retirees begin to draw lush pensions at 62? Have you noted how Congress ups and ups its unearned stipends? I am an American. I swore to a lie to get into the Spanish-American War. I bear scars on my body gained in the Islands. Therefore, I dare to denounce the scoundrels who permit over 800 poisons in our every food and drink. You will learn the true facts as we move along with the future Dr. John Marsh Pressing. What poison and how much is to be found in oranges, apples, potatoes, cabbage, onions, beets, all shipped-in winter produce from the deep South, all dairy products, all poultry and eggs, all pork, beef and mutton. In water!

We are nothing but guinea pigs to crass and criminal commercialism in the so-called science of medicine. That will be proved to you. *The question is this, what are we going to do about it?* We shall give you the testimony, under oath, given before the House Committee to study poisons in all foods. We will show you that *you* are nothing but a pawn to medical malfesance. *You have it in your hands to cor-*

rect this foul situation. What will you do, guinea pigs?

One of the last things said by that butcher, Joseph Stalin, was: "Why should we attack the Yankee pigs? The fools are poisoning themselves with the chemicals in their foods and drinks. U.S.S.R. furnishes the roach poison, fluorine.

Joe was a mad butcher, but he told the facts just before he died.)

* * *

Dr. Zollner and John made three more calls and then went back to his home for supper. The doctor sat facing the blazing logs in the fireplace, after supper, and smoked his German-made clay pipe, with the long cherrywood stem. He puffed a ring toward the ceiling and said: "John, I do not know what your religious beliefs may be. That is strictly your business. Honest religious and scientific leaders freely admit that given the proper conditions those we call dead can communicate with us that remain here. Communication is admitted by John Wesley, founder of Methodism, because he experienced it in his own home. Emanuel Swedenborg, greatest of Swedish scientists and ministers, claimed he held constant communication with spiritual beings. The Bible is a compendium of communication with good spirits and obsessions by evil spirits.

"My uncle was a general in the Civil War and often told me about Abe Lincoln's psychic experiences when he held seances in his Springfield home and in the White House. You see it was my Uncle's home in Philadelphia where Lincoln stayed one night. My 16-year-old niece was what is called a medium, and Lincoln received information through her about battles, a day or more before the news came through to Washington to government officials. Every great scientist in the last five centuries except Davy and Faraday (neither of whom would investigate) tested spirit communication, employing such means of control that trickery was impossible. My friend, you should make a thorough investigation of the subject. You see, doctors must by law view the remains and make out a death certificate. The greatest blessing he, as a close friend, can offer the bereaved relatives, is to be able to offer them concrete evidence that their dear ones have just left the old, worn-out body and stepped right into the middle of immortality.

"Every normal person has the God-given desire to live on after the great change men call death, and to be with those they loved in this earth life."

John interrupted to ask: "But doctor, do we need any more proof than we find in the Holy Bible?"

"Yes. Having seen many death bed scenes and funerals, I find that mere words in any book are not enough. Get me right, John, for I firmly believe in much of the Bible, despite the fact that there are many apparent contradictions due no doubt to incorrect translations – and the fact that there are hundreds of sects, which their adherents claim were founded on the Book, sects differing as far as the East is from the West. Paul tells is that the only thing required is faith. James, the brother of Jesus, stated that faith without works is dead. Spiritualism supplies both faith and works.

"You will discover as you study life and death and the proofs of survival over death, that the mention of such trite sayings as: 'Where they rest in hopes of blessed immortality,' is of cold comfort to a woman who sees her six-year-old darling buried from her eyes. No, John, mere words will not serve for comfort. Before many years you will find that all sects and dogmas will admit the probability of communication between our seen and their unseen worlds. I will give you a list of books, by highly reputable authors, scientists, clergymen, scientists and rulers of countries who believe in this blessed order of things. Spiritualism adds works to faith and proves there is no death. As Longfellow wrote:

There is no death; what seems so is transition.
This life of mortal breath is but the Gateway
to the Fields Elysian, whose entrance
Men call death.

(Author: The Bible is full of spirit visitations – both

good and evil spirits. The greatest scientists such as Crookes, Geley, Richet, Lodge, Doyle, Ochorowicz, Wallace, Barrett, Lombroso, Hyslop, Challis, Flammarion, Botazzi, Herlitzka, Foa, Mosso, Thury, Maxwell, Zoolner, Crawford, Hare, Edison, Morselle, Gerose, Arsakpf, Ermacore, *ad infinitum,* enforced controls such that trickery was impossible. And all wrote that they were convinced, *scientifically,* that communication could be, and was being established between those who have passed on and we who walk in fear – fear of H-bombs, bacterial warfare, poverty, death, all of which fears add up to a hell on earth. It was Shakespeare who wrote: "Hell is empty, all the devils are here."

King Charles of Sweden, Queen Victoria of British Empire, President Thiers of France, King Humbert of Italy, King George of England, King George of Greece, President A. Lincoln, President Roosevelt, President Truman – oh, one could go on for hours detailing those who have absolute certainty that you just cannot die. May we quote a bit from Jefferson's *Two Caterpillars Sitting On A Leaf?*

If we cannot fly the air like moths or millers
Are we to blame for being caterpillars?
Will that same power that doomed us crawl the earth,
A prey to every bird that's given birth,
Forgive our captor while he eats and sings,
And damn poor us because we have no wings?

Think of the moth, then the pupa, then the imago, and watch then as:

Spring comes down with all her warmth and love,
She brings sweet justice from the realm above,
She breaks the chrysallis, resurrects the dead,
Two butterflies arise encircling her head.
And so should this a lesson be
Proof of man's immortality.

On of the most significant occurences in centuries is the Sir Leslie Shane Ghost Book. It is written by a Catholic, for Catholics, and to Catholics, and proves by highly documented evidence given by many, many priests high in the Church that Spiritualism is true. Dr. Robert Hare, emeritus professor of Pennsylvania University, wrote, *Spiritualism Scientifically Proved.* Geley's *L'Ectoplasmie et la Clairvoyance* absolutely proves survival of the real man, and has photographs to prove it. In short, there are hundreds of photographs of spirits that were taken under absolute test conditions. Many were recorded on films when the photographer was not a believer, and actually took the pictures accidentally. (See TIME, February 18th, 1957. See the Catholic version of proof and the photograph of Lady Townsend who had been 'dead' for some three centuries.)

The future doctor John Marsh Pressing applied himself with great vigor to his courses in self defense and astonished his masters by his progress. John also spent many hours in the evening and nights calling on patients and visiting Chicago's slums. He went to Cook County Hospital and saw some remarkable work in surgery – but he also saw some surgery that might have been done by the corner butcher. He visited several of those damnable halls of hell called vivisection laboratories and saw man's only real friends subjected to tortures that would make skinning alive seem calm and soothing. He saw dogs beaten to death to prove nothing, dogs tumbled in barrels to prove less than nothing. Canine cavities opened and parts tied off so that necrosis could set in, and this too served no purpose.

There was one cage containing what was once a fine pointer dog. A placard gave the date when the beastly experiment to prove nothing was begun. In large letters John read: "Do not feed or water this dog." John gazed in horror as the now moribund animal spoke whole volumes with his eyes. Thirty days that noble creature had not had a drop of liquid. He asked one of the attendants what this was intended to prove, or to solve, and in what way this barbarous test was to be of help to humanity.

"None of your business," was the answer.

During his lessons in defense John had developed a grip like a pair of rail-handling tongs in a steel mill. Exasperated beyond his normal aplomb, he thrust out his right hand, hooking his fingers in the man's armpit and his thumb over the clavicle – then began closing them. The other moaned in agony but the pain was so acute he could not even attempt to defend himself. Without raising his voice John snapped: "I ask you about this dog and you had better answer or I might get out of patience with you."

"For God's sake, let up and I'll answer any question you ask me."

John released this, the Malay grip, and repeated his original question: "What is this beastly test supposed to prove?"

The fellow apparently did not know exactly what it added up to. He rubbed a new sore spot and said:

"This is proposed as some sort of test on metabolism during and after starvation. The two who run it are sons of wealthy parents and I believe they are sadists and only want to see suffering."

(Author: Shortly after this meeting two of the animal experimenters tried out one of their animal experiments on a 12-year-old boy. The crime was reported in the papers all over the world.)

That evening John went to call on Dr. Zollner at his home and told of this experience.

The doctor sighed deeply and replied: "The real criminal in these crimes are medical doctors and doctors of philosophy who serve part time, at least, as instructors in medical colleges.

"One of them who teaches in a State University stated that the torture of an innumerable number of dogs was highly laudable regardless of whether anything of value was gained for humanity. No hell could be too hot for a man, supposed to be a human being, who teaches such vile sophistry as did that villain. Every decent, honest member of the healing arts despises and abhors such infamy. I once memorized a short poem that meets with total approval:

In disobedience to our Master
We loll upon our downy beds,
While torture in the name of science,
Tears helpless animals to shreds.
And while we lie there idly dozing,
Unheeding man's friends' pain and loss
The flouted laws of Christ Redeemer
May nail us all upon the Cross.

"Yes, John, a doctor of medicine, teaching the Godly arts of healing, really said that it was good to subject any number of man's only real friends to torture, no matter how great the suffering, and no matter whether or not any humanitarian knowledge could be gained. I sometime wonder if God will some day in His infinite wisdom reverse the situation, tear man down from the high place he has stolen, and set the dogs in power. The Catholics have a great chant, taken from the Holy Bible: 'Deposuit potentes de sede Et exaltavit humiles.' (He hath thrown down the mighty from their high seat and exalted those of lowly degree).

"John, do you know that if men have souls, our lesser, now helpless brothers also have souls? The Holy Bible is literally full of proofs, absolute proofs or else we must discard the Book as being false. The first book in the Word has God making a covenant with Noah, his family and every creature. Why did He make that convenant unless there was something more than mortal about man's lesser brothers? In the last book, Revelation, it states: "And every creature that is in heaven, and on the earth, and under the earth, and such as are in the seas, and all of them heard I chanting:

" 'Blessing, and Honor, and Glory, and Power be unto Him that sitteth upon the throne. And unto the Lamb forever and ever.' And most of the books between Genesis and Revelation furnish us plenty of proof that man's animal friends and lesser brothers survive, and if desired on both sides, continue to live together. I trust that at no very future date you get a well-bred puppy and raise it. One look into the worshipping, opalescent eyes of a dog that has never been brutalized until he is almost as brutal as vivisectionists, gives the absolute lie to anybody doubting that dogs reason, plan, think, but mainly show a greater, a far greater capacity to love than any man I have ever known. I have a book I wish to give you about man' slesser brothers. Particularly I wish you to note the Weimer dogs, the Elberfeld horses. Their sagacity, their power of independent reasoning, their power to solve complex mathematical problems, plus their capacity to love, makes any honest, thoughtful man feel quite humble. The greatest scientists of Europe and some from America tested these animals and were absolutely dumfounded."

The phone rang and the doctor answered it. After listening for a few minutes he said: "Yes, I will be right over. I am bringing a colleague with me for I wish him to see and understand such a condition." Facing the young man, he said: "John, I want you to see some real cancers on another doctor's finger. They were caused by this new gadget, the X-rays. So many doctors who work with those destructive rays are getting cancer of many types. You will never forget what you are about to see. And remember this — *X-rays caused it.*"

They made ready and drove a matter of six miles to a rather nice neighborhood in the Wilson Avenue district. They stopped at a pretentious, gray sandstone residence, mounted the steps and rang the doorbell. A colored maid answered the alarm and admitted them. After leaving their hats, they mounted to the second floor and were shown into a handsome bedroom. A man of about 55 years lay moaning in pain. His right hand was swathed with heavy dressing and the odor of iodoform filled the circumambient air. The maid brought a basin of hot water and Dr. Zollner rapidly removed the bandages. For the first time John saw three X-ray induced cancers, probably sarcomas, a truly horrible sight. Dr. Zollner introduced John as a young man who was going to enter into a full medical course at the beginning of the next term, and asked the patient, an Allopathic physican named B. Abel, M.D., and a member of all of the medical societies sired by the great medical monopoly called the American Medical Association, if John might stay, examine and learn the facts about cancer which will surely completely wipe out humanity if a means was not quickly privided to prevent and/or cure it.

Dr. Abel replied: "By all means let the young neophyte remain. Perhaps he may be the God-blessed doctor who will find the cure for the disease I know I have, X-ray cancer."

Dr. Abel was surely a wonderful man who, knowing he might be another cancer death within one year, was cool and collected as he freely discussed the possibilities.

Dr. Zollner pointed out the visible subjective and objective symptoms and then said: "Dr. Abel, some very hopeful reports are being published in the German medical journals which, unlike the A.M.A. journal, does not accept actual quack remedies, nor do the German medical societies dominate elections as the home product medical society does. The last German journal explains in full the electro-coagulation of neoplasms caused by X-rays. There is no possibility of metastasis in electro-coagulation, as there is in surgery."

"What does the A.M.A. say about this technique?" demanded Dr. Abel.

"Doctor," replied Dr. Zollner, "it is small moment what the A.M.A. says or does about this technique. Better German doctors than you will find in the A.M.A. report complete healings, absolute cures. I wonder if you know that Mr. George Simmons advertised years ago that he was curing all types of malignancies in Lincoln, Nebraska? If he could then, why are we in trouble right now? Yes, Dr. Abel, I advise that we try electro-coagulation, and that it be done at once."

(Author: Dr. Abel called in an A.M.A. Allopath the next day. Biopsy was made. The pathologists could not make up their super minds whether the lesions were sarcoma, carcinoma or epithelioma. But they did advise immediate surgery. Three fingers were amputated at the hand. Metastasis set in, scattering the malignant tumor detritus over the body. Dr. Abel died within a year.

Some of the great statesmen, sportsmen, and bankers have recently died from cancer. *They let the A.M.A. doctors lead them through their whole bag of tricks – and died horribly.* In the meantime there are several known cures for cancer: the Hoxsey, the Lincoln, the Drosnes-Lazenby, the Koch, Krebiozen, et cet. The Tobey Senate Committee thoroughly investigated them, particularly the Hoxsey treatment, employing an official of the U.S. Justice Department. The report given by this one honest investigator, Benedict F. FitzGerald, clearly indicated that Hoxsey was curing all types of cancer. The report castigated the use of surgery, X-rays and radium in treating cancer. The committee also called the A.M.A. what, in its greed, it knows in its heart it is – an *oath-breaking, crooked gang for the promotion of ill-health, disease and early death.*

Here are excerpts from the FitzGerald report to the Senate Committee, the very same report that Bricker, U.S. Senator from Ohio, put out of circulation. Was he paid for this treason to God and man? Who paid him? Let us not be too, too naive. Bricker hid the report and refused to discuss it with Mr. FitzGerald. Do men do that sort of thing for chicken feed?

* * *

FITZGERALD REPORT – EXCERPTS

Thereafter, the undersigned traveled to Illinois to investigate the so-called Krebiozen controversy, and on July 2, 1953, wrote a report on his findings which is attached tereto and marked "Exhibit A." Included in this report was the evaluation:

"The controversy is involved and requires further research and development. There is reason to believe that the A.M.A. has been hasty, capricious, arbitrary, and outright dishonest, and of course if the doctrine of 'respondeat superior' is to be observed, the alleged machinations of Dr. J. J. Moore (for the past ten years the treasurer of the A.M.A.) could involve the A.M.A. and others in an interstate conspiracy of alarming proportions.

"The principal witnesses who tell of Dr. Moore's rascality are Alberto Barreira, Argentine cabinet member, and his secretary, Anna D. Schmidt."

Thereafter, the undersigned visited other areas, interrogating medical men, and on July 14, 1953, wrote a further report. Included in this was the evaluation:

This decision was handed down during the trial of a libel suit in the District Court of Dallas, Texas, by Hoxsey against Morris Fishbein, who admitted that he had never practiced medicine one day in his life and had never had a private patient, which resulted in a verdict for Hoxsey and against Morris Fishbein. The defense admitted that Hoxsey could cure external cancer but contended that his medicines for internal cancer had no therapeutic value. The jury, after listening to leading Pathologists, Radiologists, Physicians, Surgeons and scores of witnesses, a great number of whom had never been treated by any Physician or Surgeon except the treatment received at the Hoxsey Cancer Clinic, concluded that Dr. Fishbein was wrong; that his published statements were false, and that the Hoxsey method of treating cancer did have therapeutic value.

In this litigation the Government of the United States, as well as Dr. Fishbein, brought to the Court the leading medical scientists, including Pathologists and others skilled in the treatment of cancer. They came from all parts of the country. It is significant to note that a great number of these doctors admitted that x-ray therapy could cause cancer. This view is supported by medical publications, including the magazine entitled "CANCER" published by the American Cancer Society, May issue of 1948.

I am herewith including the names and addresses of some of the witnesses who testified in the State and Federal Court. It has been determined by pathology, in a great many instances by laboratories wholly disconnected from Hoxsey Cancer Clinic, that they were suffering from different types of cancer, both internal and external and following treatment they testified they were cured.

Name	Address	Type
J. A. Johnson	Ranger, Tex.	Squamous Cell No. 2
Mrs. R. J. Hickman	1225 E. Allen St. Ft. Worth, Tex.	Melanocarcinoma
Robt. Thane	Avoca, Tex.	Myxoliposarcoma
Mrs. H. H. Johnson	Denton, Texas	Adenocarcinoma
Mrs. Elmer Smith	Wellington, Tex.	Malignant melanoma
Mildred Rager	2101 Stovall St., Dallas, Texas	Melanoma
A. G. Burgess	2416 Wyman St., Dallas, Texas	Basal Cell Carcinoma
Ira Poston	5322 Victor St., Dallas, Texas	Basal Cell Carcinoma
W. E. Harmon	Grapeville, Tex.	Prickle Cell Carcinoma
Mrs. J. A. Robb	Weatherford, Tex.	Basal Cell Carcinoma
Mrs. Lessie Hester	Lubbock, Tex.	Adenocarcinoma of Uterus
Mrs. Lora Barnett	Peniel, Texas	Adenocarcinoma of Uterus
Mrs. E. E. Hockett	Farmersville, Texas, RFD	Prickle Cell Carcinoma
T. E. Truman	Waco, Texas	Epidermoid Carcinoma
Fritz Trojan	Waco, Texas	Squamous Cell type
Mr. C. W. Malone	Brownwood, Tex.	Basal Cell type

Val Seurer	Hinton, Okla.	Malignant Carcinoma
Jo Parelli	Sportotorium, Dallas, Texas	Malignant Carcinoma
Mrs. R. M. Hoffman	c-o J. B. Baird Co., Shreveport, La.	Spindle Cell Carcinoma
Tom Coates	Merkel, Texas	Basal Cell Carcinoma
J. L. Renfo	Merkel, Texas	Malignant Carcinoma
Mrs. J. D. Douglas	Ft. Worth, Tex.	Duct-cell Carcinoma
Mrs. R. S. Turner		Squamous Cell Carcinoma Grade 3
Mrs. C. E. Mallory		Squamous Cell Carcinoma
Mrs. Herman Thomas	5222 Merrimac St., Dallas, Texas	Melanocarcinoma
Clifton H. Smith	5637 Hiram St., Ft. Worth, Tex.	Malignant Carcinoma
Rev. Horace W. Irwin	West Warwick, Rhode Island	Malignant Carcinoma

I have had access to literature by leading scientists in the field of medicine. The attention of the Committee is invited to the hearings held during the 79th Congress, in July 1946; Senate Bill 1875 being under consideration, wherewith it appears, as follows:

"Dr. George Miley was born in Chicago, 1907, graduated from Chicago Latin School, 1923, graduated with B.A. from Yale University in 1927, from Northwestern Medical School, 1932, interned at Chicago Memorial Hospital in 1932 and 1933, University of Vienna Postgraduate Medical School, 1933, 1934, following which he visited the hospitals in India, China and Japan. He is a fellow of the American Association for the Advancement of Science. He holds a national board certificate and since 1945 he has been medical director of the Gotham Hospital, New York.

"Report of Dr. Miley of a survey made by Dr. Stanley Raimann (in charge of Tumor Research and Pathology, Gotham Hospital) before Senator Pepper's Committee on Senate Bill 1875, a bill to authorize expenditure of one hundred million dollars in cancer research.

"Dr. Reimann's report on cancer cases in Pennsylvania over a long period of time showed that those who received no treatment lived a longer period than those that received surgery, radium or x-ray. The exceptions were those patients who had received electro-surgery. The survey also showed that following the use of radium and x-ray much more harm than good was done to the average cancer patient."

"Dr. William Seaman Bainbridge, A.M., Sc.D., M.D., C.M., F.I.C.S. (Hon.) was the recipient of six honorary degrees from various institutions, the most recent being the degree of Doctor Honoris Cause from the University of San Marcos, Peru. He has been surgeon at the New York Skin and Cancer Hospital, Surgical Director of New York City Children's Hospital and of Manhattan State Hospital, Ward's Island, and consulting surgeon and gynecologist to various hospitals in the New York metropolitan and suburban areas.

"While there are some who still believe in the efficacy of radiation as a cure, my skepticism with regard to its value is being increasingly substantiated. But even with the best technic of today, its curative effect in real cancer is questionable. In 1939 the great British physiologist, Sir Leonard Hill wrote: 'Large doses (of gamma and hard x-ray) produced destruction of normal tissues such as marrow and lymphoid tissue, leucocytes and epithelial linings, and death ensues . . . The nation would, I think, be little the worse off if all the radium in the country now buried for security from bombing in deep holes, remains therein.'

"A neoplasm should never be incised for diagnostic purposes, for one cannot tell at what split moment the cancer cells may be disseminated and the patient doomed. Aspirating the neoplasm to draw out the cells by suction. This, too, is a very questionable procedure, for what of the cancer cells that may be present below the puncture point and around the needle which have been set free? It must be realized that while cancer cannot be transplanted from man to man, it can be transplanted in the same host."

"There is a report from another source in which Doctor Feinblatt, for six years Pathologist of the Memorial Hospital, New York, reported that the Memorial Hospital had originally given x-ray and radium treatment before and after radical operations for breast maligancy. These patients did not long survive, so x-ray and radium were given after surgery only. These patients lived a brief time only and after omitting all radiation, patients lived the longest of all."

Doctors Warned To Be Wary In Use Of X-Rays In Disease Treatments, by Howard W. Blakeslee, Associated Press Science Editor.

"New York, July 6, 1948 – X-rays and gamma rays can cause bone cancer is warning issued in 'Cancer,' a new medical journal started by the American Cancer Society. The bone cancer warning covering more than twenty pages, is by Doctors William G. Cahan, Helen Q. Woodward, Norman L. Higginbotham, Fred W. Steward and Bradley I. Coley, all of New York City.

"One of the most dangerous things about this kind of bone cancer, the report states, is the very long delay between the use of the rays and the appearance of the cancers. The delay time in the eleven cases ranged from six to twenty-two years."

"Doctor Herman Joseph Muller, Nobel Prize Winner, a world renowned scientist, has stated the Medical Profession is permanently damaging the American life stream through the unwise use of x-rays. There is no dosage of x-ray so low as to be without risk of producing harmful mutations."

If radium, x-ray or surgery or either of them is the complete answer, then the greatest hoax of the age is being perpetrated upon the people by the continued appeal for funds for further research. If neither x-ray, radium or surgery is the complete answer to this dreaded disease, and I submit that it is not, then what is the plain duty of society? Should we stand still? Should we sit idly by and count the number of physicians, surgeons and cancerologists who are not only divided but who, because of fear or favor, are forced to line up with the so-called accepted view of the American Medical Association, or should this Committee make a full scale investigation of the organized effort to hinder, suppress and restrict the free flow of drugs which allegedly have proven successful in cases where clinical records, case history, pathological reports and x-ray photographic proof, together with the alleged cured patients, are available?

Accordingly, we should determine whether existing agencies, both public and private, are engaged and have pursued a policy of harassment, ridicule, slander and libelous attacks on others sincerely engaged in stamping out this curse of mankind. Have medical associations, through their officers, agents, servants and employees engaged in this practice? My investigation to date should convince this Committee that a conspiracy does exist to stop the free flow and use of drugs in interstate commerce which allegedly has solid therapeutic value. Public and private funds have been thrown around like confetti at a country fair to close up and destroy clinics, hospitals and scientific research laboratories which do not conform to the viewpoint of medical associations.

How long will the American people take this? To illustrate the stranglehold of the American Medical Association on legislation which in turn affects every household in America, let us look at a small 25 cent tube of penicillin ointment. Is it dangerous to have around the house for a cut or small bruise on your body? Rat poison can be bought without a doctor's prescription. The sale of arsenic must have a doctor's prescription. The sale of arsenic and rat poisons is small but not pencillin. Accordingly we must have a doctor's prescription in America to buy a 25 cent tube of ointment. In Canada, however, the Medical Association has not yet discovered THE GREAT DANGER of a small tube of penicillin ointment and, accordingly the people are able to buy it without paying a doctor for a prescription. To say that it is dangerous, is silly. To assert, rather, that it is but another manifestation of power and privilege of a few at the expense of the many would be more consistent with truth and wholly accurate.

* * *

There you have the proved rascality of A.M.A. as well as that same brand of murdering conduct on the part of many Congressmen, the Food and Drug Administration and the U.S.D.A. They present some of the most brutal and contumaceous rascality the world has ever known, or ever will know. Nero, Henry VIII, Bloody Mary, Hitler and Stalin were saints compared with this aggregation of biped beasts. Listen, you who vote for name and party instead of principle and honest men. On November 20th, 1957, the report came through that the A.M.A. had determined that any person receiving Social Security shall not receive free hospitalization.

(Did you know that the A.M.A. went into the biggest lobby in Washington and forbid Eisenhower from giving the OK to increased Social Security unless and until an A.M.A. representative was placed at the summit of the Social Security Department? I voted for that man in '52 because I believed that he was a blue ribboner straight through. I'm not talking politics, or known, documented facts for fear I may land in the *oubliette* for *lese majeste.* Yes, they do that in America too, and the author has the documents to prove it. Oh, how right was FitzGerald when he said (see report) "How long is the American People going to take this from the A.M.A.?")

* * * * *

After seeing Dr. Abel, Dr. Pressing and John went each to his own bed and board. John became more determined every minute to be one honest doctor. The one grain of good wheat amidst bushels of rat droppings. He determined to study as no other medical student ever studied before, to join the A.M.A. in order to plumb the rotten apples in the barrel, then, come life or death, expose them. Day after day he took his *ju-jitsu* and *savatte* plus *le can* until the time had arrived he was mighty hard to make a point on. And nearly every evening he went to Dr. Zollner's residence, at his invitation, and made calls, absorbing far more practical medical knowledge than he would have learned in a hospital in months as an interne. Dr. Zollner had a large practice and his records of OB cases were phenomenal. He had learned in the largest lying-in hospitals in Europe, reinforced by actual experience, that Mother Nature had a way of taking care of such things in fine shape, if not interfered with by some doctor in a hurry to get through and rush off to do nothing.

John soon learned the various positions of the foetus and the presentation of the being-born baby. He was a real help in administering just the right amount of ether at the right time to relieve the sharpest pains and relax the vaginal musculature. In helping to deliver seven children there was but one small tear and the doctor soon repaired it.

One day when there was no *jitsu* practice, John went to the A.M.A. building on North Dearborn Street and found his way to the library where the Quarterly Cumulative Index of the Journal, the commercialized house organ of the medical corporation, was available. He spent hours poring over the Index and the advertisements and medical citations from all over the habitable globe.

He soon saw that one could prove almost anything by that house organ; that black was white, that food was poison, that bread once called the staff of life might better have been called the crutches of death, from the components used in making commercial bread. The stuff that had been accepted by the A.M.A. various committees was as far from the ideas and teaching of Hippocrates as heaven was from the warmed clime. There was no way of dodging the apparent fact that the Journal was out after the dollar, and heaven help the people. He found where one of the committees had condemned the use of alcoholic beverages, stating they had no place in medicine. And then he found advertisements for high alcohol content beverages and cigarettes as well as a host of what, but a few years later, the A.M.A. called quackery. There was one article condemning in most virulent and ignorant terms a device later known as Bier's Passive Hyperemia apparatus and technique, a series of cupping glasses that have given fine results in the mother's milk pump – used by millions of women on the orders of tens of thousands of A.M.A. doctors. Cupping glasses have been of enormous value in curing the bites of venomous serpents. In fact A.M.A. medicos tell people to suck a snake bite and spit out the mixed blood and venom. Bier's apparatus has positively been used successfully in frost bite, local anemias, T.B. of the male genitals, in all cases of localized anemia.

In fact, John discovered that the Journal had termed the cupping glass (when an A.M.A. man did not prescribe it) as "A Mechanical Masturbator". John also found that Bier's adaptation of the cupping glass had proved of great practical value in correcting micromastia, the female breast practically absent. And the more John went through the cumulative index and followed the citations, the more he was astounded in considering what this great heartless monopoly had gotten away with, was now, and expected for all the future to get away with – as long as the power, prestige and general domination of every human from the cradle to the grave could be stolen from the innocent or ignorant people, ably assisted by the bastard so-called *Free Press.*

John went down to Dr. Zollner's residence that late evening and reported his discoveries in malignant medicine – the kind ruled over by selfish, cruel men, not the kind established by Hippocrates and Galen.

Dr. Zollner asked John: "Did Dr. Pressing ever show you the actual proof that a medical journal, fully owned and controlled by the A.M.A. stated: 'It is better to see a man die under Allopathy, than to see his life saved by a Homepath'? Let me show you the exact truth."

He arose and after going through a considerable accumulation, picked up a medical magazine, one admittedly an A.M.A. publication, and passed it to John without comment. There it was in bold, unclean letters: "IT IS BETTER TO SEE A PATIENT DIE UNDER ALLOPATHY THAN TO SAVE HIS LIFE BY HOMEOPATHY."

John said: "Sir, will you trust me enough to take some of these records and have them photographed for my permanent record?"

"No need to do that, John, for I already have certified copies of these and many other records of Allopathic mendacity and malignancy." Dr. Zollner opened an office safe and took out a file wrapper bulging with some kind of documents.

One by one he took out, and handed to John, photographic copies of this malevolent proclamation, made by some doctor who presumably took the divine Oath of Hippocrates. Then he handed John photos made of pages from various mid-western newspapers showing George H. Simmons' claims, in bold black and white, that he was curing cancer. And copies of affidavits that Mr. A.M.A. in person, the said Simmons, had been a criminal abortionist.

"John, can you imagine the depths of degradation of a man who took good money to cure a disease he knew full well he could not cure? Who advertised he could cure cancer? Who later took over a once fairly scientific medical society and turned it into a racket? Who, once he took over the A.M.A. bounced any doctor out on his acetabulum if he dared honestly to advertise his profession?

"My boy, can you imagine the abject cowardice and humiliation every decent physician must feel when he permits that gang to subjugate him and order him what to use, and what he must not use? It just does not seem possible. It has been said, and I believe on my soul, that Simmons sold out to the great pharmaceutical houses and took cash or stock in the companies as full payment for medical treason. And this very day I believe that many top chop men in the A.M.A. have large blocks of stocks donated by these destroyers via drugs. There is the matter of the sham battle between the A.M.A. and its hatchmen, Simmons and others, and the Abbott Alkaloid Company (now Abbott Laboratories: author) headed by Dr. Abbott. That concern was putting out a very fine, ethical series of small pellets called alkaloidals. They were really a valuable addition to the doctor's armamentarium. Abbott wanted to advertise in the Journal. For an enormous amount of money paid by Abbott to the Journal, he was graciously permitted to publicize his alkaloids to the profession."

Said John: "What a bunch of knaves and thieves the A.M.A. had within its blood body then. Can this thing be proved?"

"Just take a glance at this," replied the doctor as he pulled out a photocopy of a check for $25,000.00 signed by Abbott and endorsed as paid by the officials of the A.M.A. "As of that time, I think that no greater and vicious band of brigands ever existed, because Abbott just passed the ransom price of blood on to the suffering people of the world, plus interest. John, you remember that very large drug store two blocks down the street. Many doctors insist that their patients get the prescription filled there, claiming that store furnishes superior drugs and services.

"Well, it is a known fact that that drug store adds quite a bit to every prescription in order to pay gougery to that same gang of medical goons. I have a friend who was formerly pharmacist there. When he was employed he asked how prices were figured. The store manager answered: 'We charge like hell fire and damnation, and add 17%.' I do not believe in an orthodox hell but I'll say this, No hell as imagined by the most orthodox preacher, is half hot enough for those that conspire to rob sick people. And plenty druggists and doctors do form such a conspiracy against the sick."

Doctor Zollner pulled out the evidence he had collected through many years, absolute proof of his charges. John had supper with this fine family consisting of Mom Zollner, who had formerly been a nurse trained in that finest of schools that worked hand in hand with the Frauenkrankenhaus in Vienna. Then there were three daughters, Emilie, age 18; Maria, age 16 and Hedwig, age 14, all strapping fine young women. Emilie waited table and what a table it was with that fine Old World style of cooking where the housewife did not depend on a can opener. Emilie was a decided blonde with long flaxen hair, braided a la Marguerite, hanging below her waist. John had told his parents that marriage was tabu with him, but despite his trying to bring back to his mind the tragedy of his own family, every time Emilie turned her laughing blue eyes his way, he felt himself slipping. The thought that far too soon he must be taking off for his pre-med course caused some peculiar heart symptoms. First it pounded like an old Ford T model, then seemed to descend into his well-polished boots.

After the meal, Dr. Zollner and John seated themselves before a heart-warming cannel coal grate fire and waited for the ladies to do the dishes. The doctor puffed gently at an old meerschaum he had received as a gift from a world-famous surgeon when he was taking some PG work in Germany. After a time he said: "John, you are just born for the medical profession. When you become a doctor you will perforce see many death-bed scenes that will tear at your heart. You must be kind, but never display emotion. You must be able to furnish proof that man just cannot die. He may move out of that old, wornout habitation of clay, but the spirit that God gave, and is part of God, lives on and on forever. The curse of medicine today is best explained by the old Latin adage, *Ubi tres medici, ibi duo Athei.*"

"But how is a doctor to furnish any such proof?" asked John.

"By being so assured himself that he carries conviction to those who mourn. Did you read the book on the proof of human survival by Sir William Crookes, the greatest scientist the world has ever known?"

"Yes, and I found it most intriguing. Didn't you tell me something about the psychic experiences of President

Lincoln? It seems to me that his belief should carry a great deal of weight among all Americans."

Dr. Zollner arose, went to a bookcase and came back with several old copies of *McClure Magazine* of the first decade of this century. He flipped over the pages until he came to an article, "Why We Love Lincoln," written by a highly reputable author, editor, statesman, James Creelman.

Creelman had consulted nearly all of Lincoln's old friends to get the material for his article. There was Herndon and Weik, Hay and Nicolay, Ida Tarbell, Mr. Lamon and Mr. Stoddard, all of whom were Lincoln's friends, and every one of them knew and admitted they knew that Abraham Lincoln was a Spiritualist, and believed sincerely in the probability that men today, as in the time of the Biblical Prophets, could commune with those we call dead. In fact, Creelman stated: "He saw omens in dreams, experimented with the ghostly world of Spiritualism, dreamed of his own assassination, and discussed the possibility of his being unable to fill out his second term as President."

(Author: The vision, not the dream, spoken of came true to the very finest detail.)

"Carl Schurz was a personal friend of Lincoln," said Dr. Zollner. "After Lincoln was entombed at Springfield, Illinois, President Johnson wired Mr. Schurz to come to Washington, from his home in Racine, Wisconsin, to consult about the terrific state of affairs due to the reconstruction. Mr. Schurz," continued Dr. Zollner, "stopped over in Philadelphia to visit the Tiedemanns family. Tiedemanns was a doctor, and a relative of mine, sort of an Uncle by marriage. Well, John, the 16-year-old daughter was a medium. Mediumship had come to her without any desire on her part. Mr. Schurz took part in a home seance, and the alleged spirit of the great German poet, Schiller, identified himself through this girl. Carl Schurz next asked if Abe Lincoln could be contacted. In a few moments the message came through the mediumistic girl that the spirit of Lincoln was present. Lincoln's spirit told Carl Schurz that, in the future, he would be a U.S. Senator from Missouri. Schurz stated that he was a resident of Racine, Wisconsin, and expected to live out his life span there. 'Nevertheless,' said Mr. Schurz, 'I was called to St. Louis some years later on a business deal, and in 1869 I was elected U.S. Senator from the State of Missouri.'

"John, how can all that be explained except to admit that Abe Lincoln was there in spirit? And how did that spirit know that Carl Schurz would leave his Wisconsin home and be elected a Senator from a state in which he had never considered taking up residence? As I remember it, you lean a little toward the Methodist creed. John Wesley, founder of Methodism, actually experienced spirit communications. He also wrote for his greatest sermon, The General Deliverance, that man's lesser brothers had souls that existed immortally, 'Without alloy, without interruption, and without end.' That is the way Wesley put it.

"To convince humans that there is no death, you must be fully convinced yourself that there is an immortal spirit in every creature that God created and called good. You are soon to leave us to take up your pre-medical course, and we are going to miss you very much. We hope you will keep in touch with us. Remember this: all healing arts are the noblest professions God-given to man, when honestly practiced. When the healing arts become mere money-grabbing schemes, these arts are the basest."

John was very thoughtful for a few minutes. The idea of breaking personal contact with this fine family was most devastating. The bidding adieu to that flaxen-haired Emilie was awful to consider. He blurted out like a sufferer from puppy love: "Doctor, you know something of the tragedy that happened in my family. Not many months ago I swore that there would never be a woman in my life. My family was never a happy one after the doctors operated time after time on my mother, and if you knew the full details, I am sure you would not blame me for being somewhat prejudiced. I must confess to you that after almost being a constant guest at your home where I see nothing but love, I am strongly attracted to your daughter Emilie. May I ask straight out, if you and your good wife have any objection to my corresponding with her – that is, if she is agreeable? And when possible, running up here by train to call on all of you?"

Dr. Zollner puffed slowly on his pipe and almost hid the ceiling with a nimbus of fragrant tobacco smoke before he replied: "I have a pretty good pair of eyes. So has mother Zollner. We have been taking notice of the sheep's eyes of you two. You have taken salt with us and I know you would never do anything to cause sadness in our lives. No, John, we have no objection to your writing, or your calling when it is possible for you to come up here. As the Greeks used to say: 'Our lives are in laps of the gods.' Take two young people like you and Emilie, permit things to take the normal course and there is but one logical ending. No proposals, you understand. No vows. While you are in college, you will meet many other women. Emilie will meet many men. What will be, will be."

* * *

John received many letters from Dr. and Mom Pressing while he was in Chicago. The doctor had been to see the officials at the college where John was to take his pre-med, and arranged that John could enter at any time. Frankly the President of the school often wondered what assistance might be gained by a knowledge of things that had no known relation to the daily grind of a physician's life. Make a gentleman of a gentleman? In fact, as the good man knew, there were young gentlemen he personally contacted who came as gentlemen to his college, joined a frat, future, after graduation, to the highest bidder. In truth, went into football on a broad scale, then sold their whole

some of them even while in his college began selling themselves to throw a football game. No, two years pre-med is nothing but a *means adopted by the* A.M.A. *and the Carnegie people to cause a shortage of physicians.*

(Author: It is being argued by those who should know right today, and for some time back, that the Carnegie people are notably perversive. If you have read the newspapers, you know this to be factual. There are those doctors, and their names are legion, who admit that the A.M.A. leaders are sold out body and soul, if any, to the German Nazi dye industry and their American suppliants. *Why does the A.M.A. and the F.D.A. fight an investigation? What villainy do they fear will be exposed?* Remember the FitzGerald report that castigates the two mentioned for dishonesty, rascality, withholding of known cancer cures, conspiracy and other crimes and misdemeanors. Was Senator Bricker paid to hide, or perhaps destroy the FitzGerald report? Who paid him? How much? *If he had a drop of honest blood in his carcass, would he not demand an investigation of his conduct in defending and shielding rascals in government, and any organization that willfully and deliberately withholds known facts?* Does Bricker not realize that all of the A.M.A. doctors and surgeons could do nothing for Vandenberg, Taft, and other senators? And the men who stabbed Taft in the back, what of them?)

All too soon John had to leave his dear friends in Chicago, run home for a few days to visit with his Dad and Mom and then off to his pre-medic course. This was not the type of case described in Shakespeare's Seven Ages: "Next the whining school boy, with his satchel and shining morning face, creeping like snail unwilling to school." John was what one might say, "rarin' to go" for an honest degree as Doctor of Medicine.

CHAPTER 8

THE PRE-MEDICAL RACKET

The meeting of John and his adopted parents was not without emotion. He stayed with them for several days during which time he had many secret conferences with Ma Pressing. He showed her a photo of Emilie Zollner and confessed that he was falling for her like tons of bricks. Ma was delighted, after making quite a study of the beautiful girl looking her straight in the eyes. She saw in that face, physical and mental, a soul looking out through the windows of a soul.

"John, dear, don't you let that girl get away from you! She will make the best of wives to a doctor, for I see selflessness, loyalty, trust, confidence, without jealousy peering at me."

John agreed at every point.

"Have you spoken to Emilie's parents yet?" she asked.

"Well, I did bring up the matter. Dr. Zollner agreed we could correspond and I could come to see her occasionally. I can take the Flyer to Mexico about 11 P.M. and be at the Zollner home before 8:30 the next morning. The service back is even better, so that will permit me to spend two days with Emilie at least once a month. No, mother Pressing, I shall not let her get away from me, God willing."

John made a number of calls with Dr. Pressing and examined a large amount of documentary evidences he had collected throughout the years. Every record pointed the finger of shame and disgrace at the corporation without soul, the American Medical Association. As he drove around with Dr. Pressing, John related some of the incidents he had experienced in the smoggy city but was particularly communicative in speaking of what he had discovered in the cumulative index in the library of the medical association. He constantly came back to the question: "Why do doctors permit themselves to be hoodwinked into accepting what constitutes a sort of serfism?"

Dr. Pressing replied: "That question is now agitating a great many excellent doctors. They see the many remedies that have been of great service, when combined with advice as to diet and exercise, not to speak about mental and physical relaxation, that rascality has expunged from materia medica. I will not, at this time, puzzle you with abstruse information, but I will say this: a great doctor in Europe wrote: 'Some patients get well with the doctor and his drugs; some get well without the doctor and his drugs; more get well in spite of the doctor and his drugs.' "

"Isn't that a kind of medical nihilism?" asked John.

"Call it what you like, John, but it is true to a great extent. The only real medicine is preventive medicine and strict sanitation. The Black Plague that killed 25 million people in Europe was brought to a halt, not by medicine, but by sanitation. If doctors would advise people wisely about their diet, their habits, their daily living, and if people would follow good advice, there would be a reduction of more than 65% of all illnesses. The natural condition of a living being is health, not disease. And Nature naturally will restore health if she is given a fair chance. I look forward with considerable anxiety as I see doctors gradually discarding the old, proved specific botanical healing agents. It is very remarkable that the really great drugs were discovered and first used by the unlearned.

"Modern pharmaceutical houses are taking the proved remedies and extracting what they call the alkaloids and glucosides without taking thought what valuable remnants there may be left in the crude drug.

"Well, son, tomorrow you enter college for your premed course. I have written a letter of introduction for you to hand to Dr. Rice, a most excellent gentleman, despite the fact that he did not fritter away two years in a premedical course. Furthermore, he is one of the best physicians in the state. He is an Eclectic doctor, that is he tries to use the best remedy for any given patient, regardless of whether it is an Allopathic matter or a Homeopathic remedy. He wants results for his patients, and he gets results. He is over-worked, and yet when I drove over to see him a few weeks ago, he asked me to urge you to spend as much time with him as you can spare from your studies.

"He has a greater store of Latin, Greek, chemistry and other pre-medical qualifications than any man in the medical societies. Be sure and contact him at once when you reach his town. There is a silly rule at the college that Freshmen must wear a green cap. Wear it with as much grace as you can muster. American colleges nowadays are going crazy about sports, forgetting in the act that the students are supposed to be there for education. Many students are ruined for life in football scrimmages, so I'd forget it. If any of the students resent the fact and attempt to haze you, well, I am glad you took the courses in *ju-jitsu* and *savate*. Anybody who attacks you will be mighty sorry. In protecting yourself, never lose your temper. Let your opponent lose his and lose the battle."

The next morning John took the 7:15 train and was at the registrar's office early. In due time he entered the various studies that were to be open sesame to medical college. He went that evening to see Dr. Rice, a half hour before he had to go to the station for his home. Dr. Rice was a very pleasant person, a man who inspired confidence. He seemed a well-preserved 65. On the spot, after talking to John for a quarter hour, he invited him to make calls with him when he was not in class.

* * *

Dr. Rice had considerable influence with college authorities, a fact that obtained many favors for John, such as skipping certain studies with which he was as well-informed as the instructor.

John was now a handsome young fellow, built like an

athlete, swift on his feet, and before many days the coach (who received a much larger salary then the college president) called on him to invite him to make the football squad. John refused politely.

"I came here to get pre-medical as soon as I possibly can. Sorry, but I will have no time for sports."

The coach tried to coax him by various oily arguments. He would be a sissy. The student body would not like his refusal. No girl would pay the least attention to him. He would never get the coveted big letter W on his sweater.

John was adamant. The coach became angry, then furious, insulting. John turned his back and started away. The coach made an awful mistake when he caught John by his right shoulder and spun him around and attempted to slap his face. That *was* a grave error. John simply grasped his wrist, brought it over his shoulder as he turned his back to the coach, and hurled him over the shoulder. Quite a number of students saw the whole affair. John turned his back and walked away.

There was an investigation because such a thing cannot be hid under the bushel. John was completely exonerated and the coach abjectly apologized. A number of students who were thinking of hazing the young doctor-to-be suddenly changed their minds and became very respectful.

More, a number of students went to the college prexy and asked that a class in defense be organized, with John in charge. Many young co-eds tried to inveigle John into asking for dates. Always with that flaxen-haired, modest Emilie before his mind's eye, John did not fall for them. He agreed with the President to form a small class and instruct worthy young folks in the art of defense. Young women students besought him to become members. That too was arranged and eight co-eds joined the class. One thing John provided, that every young woman must be chaperoned and that the girls must dress modestly. Thus all the young folks got a lot better exercise than playing in any sport, and the training might save lives.

One girl showed great promise in *ju-jitsu* and that saved her life. She lived on the south side in Kansas City and went home every week end. Some time after she had become proficient in *ju-jitsu,* she went home on Friday evening late. She alighted from a Woodland Avenue car and took a short cut that brought her in at the back entrance.

The whole family, except the father who was a conductor on the K.C. Southern Railway, had gone to church, leaving the house empty. Mary March, the lady in question, unlocked the door and entered. She smelled cigar smoke and wondered who had been in. She found out when a large, vicious negro housebreaker seized her by the throat and began throttling her. It took less time for her to bring things under control than it has taken you to read this. The ruffian came to on the floor face down, his right arm twisted over his back behind him. He was absolutely helpless while she applied the twist.

(Author: How do I know this? I lived next door north and heard Mary screaming for help. I ran over with a shotgun and took over, while Mary called the police.

This is just another proof of the value of such means of attack and defense instead of the highly commercialized football, basketball, golf, tennis and the like. One hour of *l'escrime* (fencing) will do more for the making of healthy, moral, long-lived future generation than all these college sports, which at best lose millions of study hours every year, and have been bastardized by being taken over, root, stock and branch by racketeers. And imagine if you can this: *coaches get higher salaries than college presidents. And we complain because Russia got the first Sputnik into the air,* Shakespeare had a word for it: "What fools we mortals be."

I have kept a cross-indexed file of documentary evidence for about 50 years, all covering the fields of the various healing arts. Since the man from Ohio, who for some reason known only to God is still in the United States Senate, hid or destroyed the work of Senator Tobey's Committee demanding a rigid investigation of the workers of Satan who have tried by every possible means to withhold known cancer cures from suffering humanity, many prolific doctors, with a flair for writing – whether true, or not, have been spreading the villainous propaganda that the only hope in cancer, is surgery, X-rays and/or radium.

One of these kind of doctors, who like Morris Fishbein, has probably never had a patient in his medical career, writes a medical column for the *Chicago Tribune* – one Dr. Van Dellen. And just like the Journal of the A.M.A., he often makes statements, and later, like many a good A.M.A. fellow, changes like the proverbial weather cock. I have clips of his columns in which he condemns insecticides, then accepts them. He condemned antibiotics (blunder-drugs) and now advises their use in practically every condition from pip to phimosis. A true A.M.A. disciple (is he a disciple of Hippocrates?), he damns known cancer treatments that succeed after A.M.A. type treatments fail.

Consider the man's column in the *Tribune* of November 27th, 1957. He actually admits half truths. Why doesn't he go the whole way? It appears that one can get away with anything if he is a writer for "THE WORLD'S GREATEST NEWSPAPER." Van Dellen tells in this issue the horrifying records of smoking tobacco and rot-gut booze. Effects actually horrifying to the Nth degree, in these days of America – America ruled by gangsters and racketeers in government and commercialism, and commercialism defines the A.M.A. 100%. We have a F.D.A. that crawls on its collective bellies before the drug makers and the drug dopers of the A.M.A. I defy each of them, or all of them, to meet me in public debate, each bringing their records. My records will be quite largely from the A.M.A. Journal, and/or A.M.A. doctors. Agents for some of these most unAmerican gangs have several times burglarized my homes and laboratories. They have set fire to one home and fired at least three laboratories. Some of them claiming by their own confession before witnesses to be agents for the Dannenberg Detective Agency, Chicago, Illinois, stated they were hired by the A.M.A. and the Wisconsin Alumni Research Association, to "get" me.

Let us now consult a few of Van Dellen's blurbs. A 1957 issue of the *Tribune* quotes the proofs furnished by many medical authorities, that smoking and drinking makes their slaves far more liable to have cancer than those who abstain. Van Dellen quotes Sandowsky, who studied 2500 cases confined to government hospitals. Sandowsky absolutely proves to anybody but the A.M.A. and the U.S. Food & Drug Administration, that tobacco smoking is the etiological factor in the absolutely horrifying increase of cancer. And yet, the A.M.A. and F.D.A. have persecuted, blacklisted, maligned and tried by every means to make real cancer cures unavailable. I defy, challenge either of these organizations, or both together, to deny the truth of these charges. Why didn't the A.M.A. type cancer treatments save Taft, Vandenberg, Babe Zaharias, Babe Ruth?

Before me, as I write this, I see numbers of clippings from the *Tribune,* on the word of Van Dellen, strong condemnations of antibiotics lovingly touted by such sheets as the *Tribune,* Los Angeles *Times,* Kansas City *Star,* and practically every paper served by Associated Press. But always, a few days later we find these mendacious writers have turned straight about and urge the use of these 'blunder drugs'. Are all of them not like the character described in Holy Writ? Read with me this from 2 Kings 18:27: Hath he not sent me to speak these words? Hath he not sent me to men which sit on the wall (fence, of indecision, rascality and medical manslaughter. Author) that they may eat their own dung and drink their own piss? What else are the A.M.A., the F.D.A., congressmen, the so-called free press, doing but mouthing their own excrementa?

If you are a man of family, one out of five in that family are going to die with cancer. The A.M.A. and F.D.A. forbid them to have a chance of living through the administration of Hoxsey treatment, Drochnes-Lazenby treatment, the Koch, the Lincoln, or several other treatments that *have* cured all types of cancer.

But, returning to the man Van Dellen, who claims his blurbs (true or false?) are heard by 12,000,000 Americans every day. He tells of the researches of Drs. Wynder and Bross of the Sloan-Kettering institute, Reports that the smoking of tobacco is the principal cause of cancer. How can our Congressmen sleep – except at their desks where bills have been pending for years pointing out the cancer stimulating chemicals in every single thing we eat, drink and breathe. Why has Congress done nothing? When will all of us wake up and demand the elimination of poisonous chemicals from our foods and drink?

For your children's sakes and their children's sakes, if you do not care about your own life, *wake up! Act!* Can nothing arouse you? As FitzGerald, U.S. Department of Justice, put it: "How long will the American public take this?" He was talking of the treasonable activities of the A.M.A. and F.D.A., and possibly a section of the USDA, the gang that permitted poison in flour for nearly twenty-five years. There is no doubt that this chemical, very liberally used, produced epilepsy in uncounted cases as shown by the use of the electro-encephalograph on test animals whose reaction must be the same as humans. If it was not poison, why did the government order its use stopped? Why did the government permit its use in the first place? These statements are all matters of public records. And the future Dr. John Marsh Pressing will learn of the addition of at least 800 highly questionable chemicals made from coal tar in every thing Americans eat, drink and breathe.

Some time ago Van Dellen, in the *Tribune*, ran an article telling of men, not physicians, he said, who learned a mess of medical slumgullion, and then used it against scientific medicine. Scientific medicine, my elbow! Medicine is not a science; it is pure empiricism, trial and error. Did you ever go to an A.M.A. doctor and consult him about anything from alopecia to zoophilla? He gives you a prescription, you take it, get worse, call on the doctor, he tries something else until nature cures you, or the doctor's fantastic prescriptions kill you. *Trial and error.* However, medicine, worthily and honestly practiced, is the noblest of all professions. But it would be far better if it called to its aid, Chiropractic, Osteopathy, Nature. I declare again, I can take the writings of Van Dellen and the column of the Journal of the A.M.A. and I can prove anything under the sun. And this person dares speak about anybody condemning scientific medicine.

Scientific medicine! The word science comes from the Latin verb meaning "to know." Look over the history of medicine of the last two thousand years. The Black Plague, said one great medical scientist, was caused by too-frequent bathing. Hah! Bathing and sanitation, not medicine, brought the Plague to a sharp ending. Medical science once prescribed teas made from the feces of animals. Scientific medicine used to bleed patients for healing. It bled George Washington to death when he was suffering from quinsy (ulcerative tonsilitis). It is better than an even bet they Abe Lincoln would not have died from the bullet of Wilkes Booth, if science in the form of many doctors had not intervened. Let scientific medicine explain, honestly, why a certain President's ileum was resected at the ileo-cecal valve, and then joined by an anastomosis at the median section of the transverse colon, instead of making the union just about the ileo-cecal valve in the ascending colon, or cecum.

Re the present situation of the same President. The great medical scientists at the great Ford institution declared, according to radio broadcast on November 27th, 1957 *that cases like the present should not have anti-coagulant administered. Dr. White ordered anti-coagulants to the President, and he got a clot in a cerebral artery that fed the speech center of his brain.* And from what particular condition, arose the clot (embolism) that was small enough to pass through the lungs and heart to lodge in the brain? Let medical science give us the fact – that is, if it knows the fact, which seems to be in great controversy between medical scientists.

Ah yes, all of us are going to learn much of this thing, dubbed by non-scientific scientists, medical science, as we follow the factual career of an actual aspirant to the honor and the glory of *true* medicine, *honestly* practiced, one John Marsh Pressing.)

* * *

The rushing by train to and from the college town was taking too much time from John's classes, so it was decided that he would stay in the college town all week days, returning to his home with Doctor and Ma Pressing week ends. Now, this college had been noted for its sports, more than its sciences, for a number of years, and sports racketeers and newspaper writers had been making no small amount of money out of the college football team. This source of revenue began falling off as the student body became more and more enamored with the courses in *ju-jitsu, savate* and *l'escrime* John had established. And, not strange to say it, the physical condition of the students had been better than in the history of the college. Why? Because most college sports are sheer brutality and milliards of muscles are not used or developed. The racketeers did not like the chipping off of their revenue. It is probable that the coach had a hand in what developed shortly.

At the beginning of the next semester, a burly roughneck-appearing individual entered the college, sponsored by the disgruntled coach, who saw himself out of a nice graft if the sports thermometer could not be raised to the former fever heat. This party, Sam Wood, started right in in an attempt to break up the classes founded by John. He claimed he was from Kansas City, and as Mary March, the girl who overcame the negro burglar, lived in that great city, John asked her to look up this man's record next week end while she was home.

The following Monday she sought John and revealed that Wood was a roughhouse wrestler, a kicker in the belly, and eye gouger. And that he was known as the 'bone-breaker', because he had done quite a bit of bone breaking.

On every possible occasion, Wood bumped violently into John and tried to pick a rough and tumble fight. John carefully avoided that because he wanted plenty of witnesses to this ape's conduct before the time came to dispense with his presence among decent people. One may judge of Wood's background when we assure you that he pronounced 'bird' as 'boid', 'first' he called 'foist', and third', 'thoid'. His strength was enormous, and that is just the endowment that makes such a man easy pickings for one adept in *jujitsu,* or *savate.* John knew that there must be a showdown before very long so he kept a watchful eye on Wood, measuring his probable method of attack, and preparing his defense. The end came quicker than he had expected. The 'bone breaker' regularly went to Kansas City and always brought back cheap whiskey with him. This he ladled out in small quantities to some of the weaker vessels in the student body. But he gulped down the large libations.

One Monday morning John arrived at the gym a bit late because his train was delayed by a wreck. As he sprinted up the gym steps, Wood rushed out of the door and collided with him.

Wood cursed John and growled: "Why don't you look where you're going?"

"Sorry, friend," said John as he attempted to walk around the bully and enter the gym.

Wood grabbed the lapels of John's overcoat and shook him violently and growled: "I've got a good mind to break you in two pieces and let the dogs gnaw you."

"Well, perhaps you might do it, and again – you might have bad luck," said John without raising his voice. "Now suppose you release my coat lapels and go on your way."

"I'm going to mop the steps with your carcass," roared the bully.

The confusion had attracted plenty of witnesses as another Sampson was just about to take a fall.

Wood shook again. John reached out and took him by the lapels of his coat with a firm grip. He then fell backward, as Kuwo had so well taught him, dragging Wood with him. In the act of falling he doubled up both legs at the knees, planted his feet in Wood's belly and neatly tossed him to a distance of some five feet, over John's head. Just like that. And just as easy for one who knows self defense, instead of goal defense. Wood was out cold. John entered the gym, caught up a pail and filled it with icy water, went out and dashed it over the bully's sweetly-sleeping carcass. Investigation showed the hook-up between the coach and a K.C. gambling ring. His and Wood's faces were notably absent from the ivy-clad walls of C.W. College thereafter.

A year rapidly passed into history. John had been to Chicago three times to see Emilie Zollner, and every time it took all his will power to hold back his confession of love. And every parting was apparently tearing at the hearts of both of them. Dr. Zollner and Ma Zollner could not have helped knowing that the inevitable was bound to happen, but they said nothing to disclose their awareness.

When it was found expedient that John should spend some of nights at his college town, Dr. Rice insisted that he spend them at his home — another home ruled by deep love and understanding. He was making more and more calls with the doctor, and his knowledge of real medicine increased astronomically. One rather stormy day, a patient called at the office with an upper arm swelled to at least twice its normal dimensions. It seemed that some physician, a loyal A.M.A. member, had advised a shot of some kind of vaccine.

He had not taken time to sterlize his hypo needle and had infected the patient with some sort of mixed infection. He was in fearful pain, and the infected area was apparently full of pus, as was demostrated by its softness and motility under pressure. Of course the patient felt feverish and ugly, and very resentful toward the apostle of science who had been so very unscientific. There was one thing to do and

Dr. Rice, ably assisted by John, did it. The area was washed and sterilized with kolesol, and lanced. A great quantity of pus was obtained and the patient was immediately relieved from the severe pressure pain. The wound was washed out with kolesol solution, and dressed with a moist dressing of this same antiseptic. Dr. Rice asked the patient to wait in the outer office for a short time while he prepared certain medicines.

"John, come with me as I want to show you how Dr. Duncan prepared the most valuable remedy in all cases of pyogenic infection that medicine has ever known." The technique of this autogenous, specific vaccine is remarkably simple and one of the wonders of modern medicine is that high power medicos do not use the best specific there is. And it is nature's way indeed. Dr. Rice took a portion of the pus and carefully attenuated it by heat. He then mixed a quantity of the attenuated bacteria with distilled water, colored it with a vegetable dye for psychological reasons, and directed the patient how it was to be taken.

He was to wash the wound twice daily with kolesol solution and let nature do the work. The bowels were to be kept rather loose with castor oil, the arms given a rest until his next visit in three days. That was all, positively all, no shots, no foreign drugs, no coal tar trash, just keep the area covered with a most dressing of kolesol.

(Author: The patient fully recovered in a week. This case personally known to the author was typical. And the very unconscionable medical rascal who did this mal-practice, had even suggested to the patient that he might have to amputate his arm.)

The second day after the last mentioned case, while John was attending class, Dr. Rice called at the college and asked the President to dismiss John for the balance of the week, as he was needed to save a life. The permission being granted, the doctor and John drove out into the country about ten miles and turned into a smooth gravel road that led to a large brick farm home. As they had driven along, Dr.

Rice had briefed his disciple on the case, and what part he was to take in it.

It was a serious case of puerperal sepsis, otherwise known as child-bed fever, and a killer far too often.

(Author: when Dr. Oliver Wendell Holmes, a great physician, author and poet, had stated, some time previously, that this condition was contagious, medical men almost blew him sky-high. The great man was cruelly persecuted, mainly by one of the cubs of the A.M.A. tiger, in Massachusetts. Even men accredited with being great doctors at Yale and Harvard, acted as if Dr. Holmes was what they called a quack. But Holmes was proved right 100%. The name of Oliver Wendell Holmes will shine for uncounted centuries as a luminary of the first magnitude. It required many, many hours of research for the author to find the names of his traducers And even more time to discover any startling discovery, or work that his traducers and calumniators ever did. As Sir Walter Scott sang it, they died 'Unwept, unhonored and unsung'.)

So as Dr. Rice and John drove along, the doctor said: "This is a case of puerperal sepsis. The patient is in real jeopardy. It is evident that the doctor or nurses at the hospital at C........ were not clean, or sanitary. If the truth were known, I'll wager it would show that the attending doctor had just come from a case of sepsis without taking the proper precautions. In making a digital examination, he could readily have transmitted the invaders. And now that doctor can not be contacted and we are called in to save his carcass, that is, if we can. There are two things we must do, if we are to succeed. We must again use Duncan's really scientific discovery. And the infected area must be raised to a temperature of 106°, and kept there for at least 48 hours, or at least until her temperature drops to nearly normal."

John interrupted to ask, for confirmation of previous data, what the Duncan technique consisted of, and how the doctor discovered it.

"As I get it," replied Dr. Rice, "he had a dog that received a severe injury to a front paw. As Duncan was quite fond of the canine, he treated the wound as he would have treated a human being. The dog got worse and Duncan thought it would surely die. Duncan was called out of town because of a serious car accident to one of his relatives. He glanced at the dog just before he set forth and surmised that the dog would die within a few hours. He noticed that the dog was weakly chewing at the dressings, so Duncan removed them thinking to let the animal pass away in peace. The dog immediately began licking the wound. Duncan had to rush off.

"Well, you may imagine his shock when he came back three days later and found the animal on his feet, tearing into a dish of food he had not touched before the doctor left. The dog seemed famished for both food and drink. The dog made an almost miraculous recovery.

"Duncan put his mind to work. Was there some antiseptic action in the saliva? Or did the swallowed bacteria-containing pus stimulate some sort of healing process, the *Vis Naturae Medicatrix?* After long observations of other wounded dogs, he found that, if the animal could reach the wound with his tongue, that dog was going to recover. He decided it was the bacteria in the pus that brought about the curative action. He next began trying out this reaction on humans suffering from Brights, from gonorrhoea, from puerperal septicemia, in fact, a great variety of conditions, and found this natural method the nearest to a specific he, or for that matter, any other doctor, had ever known.

"Now, John, the A.M.A. to the contrary notwithstanding, I know that most fevers are nature's attempts to destroy the invaders. Of course any doctor who is fit to practice, knows that no form of artificial, or sun heat should be used on a patient who is at a certain stage in pulmonary T.B. But in pyogenic infections, and in other types of infections we meet in practice, *heat* is essential because it brings on active leucocytosis and hyperemia of freshly oxygenated blood.

The greatest medical crime to date is the dunking of patients suffering from typhoid fever into ice water. Every man who has used, or is now using that technique, should be tried for criminal malpractice. If the patient dies, he should be charged with murder.

"Regarding the patient we are calling on, I want you to stay right with her and apply heat as I shall show you, while I take the secretion from the genitalia back to town and prepare a quantity of autogenous vaccine according to Dr. Duncan's directions." As he finished speaking they drew up before the door of the house. Doctor Rice handed John a package which he said contained the apparatus for the hydrotherapy for the patient, Mrs. White. They were conducted into the house and into the sick chamber. Dr. Rice rapidly took the case history, while at the same time checking the heart, respiration, pulse and temperature. It appeared to him to be a typical case of septicemia following a bad job, on someone's part, in the ecouchment.

Temperature 104.5; pulse somewhat dichrotic, rate 94, not too strong, thready at times. Symptoms of any number of diseases, but with the case history of careless, or was it reckless, obstetrics, the diagnosis was positive. The patient also spoke of some hypodermic injection the doctor had given her. Possibly some ecbolic, thought Dr. Rice, and unneeded, if he knew his OB, and hundreds of women patients would have sworn he did. The apparatus for applying the moist heat was simple: a five gallon container for the hot water at about 107 degrees. A special vaginal rubber appliance through which the hot water passed, thence to a slop jar. A kolesol douche was made immediately after the doctor had taken some of the secretion for his autogenous vaccine – which was to be administered orally, Nature's way. The orificial rubber bag was then slipped into place, the tank was filled with water of the proper temperature, the real scientific practice of medicine began, with John, the doctor-to-be, in charge. He was not, said Dr. Rice, to stop the treatment for a moment unless the patient had to use the bed pan. Then the doctor took off for town.

He came back in six hours and could note already that the patient showed some improvement in pulse and a slight drop in her temperature.

He administered the first dose, by mouth, of the autogenous vaccine, and stayed an hour to see if there would be any unfavorable reaction. There was none. He directed John to keep up the hydrotherapy and vaccine by mouth. As he left he said: "One of the best practical nurses in the section will be out to relieve you in probably three hours. She is an old-timer in nursing and knows just what to do. Her husband will bring her and you can come back to town with him."

John carried on and was back in town by 11 P.M., reporting that the patient's temperature had dropped to 99.5°.

After he had reported this to Dr. Rice, that real disciple of Hippocrates shook John's hand warmly and remarked: "You are going to make one doctor in a hundred thousand. You were born to be a doctor. Ma Rice left a nice, warm supper in the kitchen. Let's eat."

(Author: This patient's temperature was normal in 30 hours. She had no side and no terminal, or future-threatening complications. The whole human race is being threatened by the so-called "wonder" drugs. Many honest, wise doctors predict catastrophic effects in the years to come. Is that what is happening today? Why are all of the degenerative diseases increasing at super-sonic rates despite the billions of dollars that have been spent to prevent and/or cure them? Come, scientific doctors, tell us why. And do not insult our intelligence by pulling that old chestnut about better diagnostic methods, for diagnosis is only about one-half of the clinical picture. The clear, plain facts remain that man's great killers are just out of control. And an equally evident fact is that medical and commercial drug monopolies must stand before the bar of Divine Justice to answer for their crimes – the most vicious crimes the world has seen.

In the last ten years hundreds of the highest type doctors, after studying thousands of cases, have announced in print that cigarettes are the prime cause of lung cancer, Buergher's disease, and are interdicted in many forms of the world's greatest killer – heart disease. Now *Mr. F.D.A., and Mr.* A.M.A., *why do you not issue press releases to these facts you know?* Mr. A.M.A. why did you print a lead article by the great tumor specialist, Dr. Ochsner, setting forth these facts *to doctors only,* and then persecute and villify men who *are* curing cancer? In view of these known facts, Mr. F.D.A. why did you placard every U.S. Postoffice with a lying diatribe against the Hoxsey treatment?

Senator Bricker, how can you sleep at night after you hid or destroyed the official report by FitzGerald, a report proving the rascality of governmental drones, and the American Medical Association? A report definitely proving Hoxsey is curing cancer? Don't you know, or has the A.M.A. pistol at your head, that MAN magazine sent a representative thoroughly to investigate cancer patients quite evidently cured by Hoxsey after A.M.A. doctors sent them to die? Don't you know that other, but apparently honest, government men have announced that far over 50% of the reports made by diagnostic laboratories cannot be depended on? Mr. Bricker, you are an old man and will soon be called on to answer for your acts in sentencing uncounted thousands of your fellow men to death. What could A.M.A. type medicine do for Babe Zaharias, Babe Ruth, and many of your colleagues in the Senate?

Mr. FitzGerald, one honest government man, definitely pointed out that there was evidently an inter-state conspiracy of alarming proportions concerning cancer cures that were curing cancer. Bricker, are you one of the parties to that conspiracy? If you are a conspirator, why not shrive your guilty soul *now*. Is that piddling office you hold of such great moment and importance that you are willing to risk thousands of years of your life to come to receive the adulation of your co-conspirators against human life? Be a man, a decent, an honest man. Read the FitzGerald report, if you have not destroyed government property, illegally. We have noted many times that you launch out against Communism. The maddest Communist is an angel of mercy when compared to men who deliberately subject their brothers to tortures that make Nero's best saintly by comparison. May God have mercy on your soul, for you will need it, if you are in conspiracy to withhold positive cancer cures from suffering humanity.)

John, the future doctor-to-be, returned to college the next morning. He found a letter awaiting him from Dr. Zollner's beautiful daughter, Emilie. They were exchanging at least two letters every week now, and John found it more and more difficult to abstain from throwing all his life into one basket and rushing up to Chicago to propose marriage to her. True, he had tacitly promised Dr. Zollner that he would not ask the girl to make definite promises as yet. Possibly the doctor did not now realize the turbulent, overwhelming love that John entertained for her.

After the college term was over, John went to visit his folks for three days. He confided his heart symptoms to Mother Pressing and that lady, wise in the ways of men and maidens, advised him to go, forthwith, to Emilie and to take along an engagement ring. You see, Mother Pressing had been in correspondence with Emilie, and knew that the girl was, forgetting all others, centering her maiden affections and her whole life on John, for better – never for worse, for she had never before looked longingly at any other male.

Without sending word of his intended visit, John caught the Flyer at Mexico and landed in Chicago early next morning. He went at once to Marshall Field's jewelry department and purchased a magnificent engagement ring. He next took a taxi to Emilie's home and found them preparing an early lunch because the doctor had a number of tubercular patients in the slums to call on.

Many times Dr. Zollner had spoken of John as a mighty fine man, physically and mentally and said longingly:

"Mother, I wish we had a son just like John to carry on in the practice of real, honest medicine." Emilie was in the kitchen preparing another course and could not have possibly heard her father say: "I have a feeling that John will be up to visit us before long. My, what wouldn't I give for a son like him."

Mother Zollner smiled archly at him and remarked: "Papa, perhaps you will have a son just like John. Who knows?" (She had been reading John's letters to Emilie, and wise lady that she was, surmised John would be as dear a son to them, as if he had been born their son.)

Before the doctor could make a reply, the door bell rang and Emilie went to answer it. She opened the door and gazed at John with her very soul in her eyes. "I'm so glad to see you, John," she said as she shook hands.

The touch of her hand went through John like an electric shock of a million electron volts. He could no longer hold back the torrent of his love. He closed the door behind him, faced Emilie and without a word swept her into his arms.

She drew him tight to her swelling bosom and moaned: "Darling, I've missed you so, so terribly."

Mother Zollner glanced archly at the doctor and remarked: "Papa, unto us is born a son!"

CHAPTER 9

"PHYSICIAN HEAL THYSELF"

"And a certain woman which had an issue of blood twelve years. And had suffered many things of many physicians, and had spent all she had, and was nothing bettered, but rather grew worse." —
Luke

After the first transports of the couple and her family had moderated a bit, the whole family sat down to enjoy a genuine German lunch. Emilie was rather awestruck as she glanced constantly at the Wesselden diamond that outshone the headlight of the Super-Chief.

After finishing lunch, Dr. Zollner said to Emilie: "Liebschen, you are going to be a doctor's wife – soon I hope, for we cannot let our new son escape – and as such you must remember that a real doctor's time can scarcely be called his own. But, if I had a thousand lives to live, I would be a doctor in every life, had I the choice. John is going to make a doctor in a hundred thousand, and that means that you will have to spend many lonesome hours.

"You must realize that any man, regardless of his method of healing, if he does heal, is nature's nobleman. The success of a man engaged in the healing arts depends very much on his wife. I want you always to follow in the footsteps of your mother. Jealousy in a doctor's wife is the silliest emotion of the female heart. The inordinately jealous wife can so unman her husband and distract his mind from his patients, that it may cause deaths. I have known of many cases wherein I am positive such foolish displays of immature and childish emotion have so befogged the doctor's judgment that his best, under the circumstance, was far too little. Never forget that, child. And now, Son, I am going to drag you away from a mighty fine lady for a few hours. Right now is a rare opportunity to see some TB cases."

From the way John and Emilie embraced each other, one

might have the idea that he was being banished to the South Pole. Dr. Zollner waited patiently with a smile of vast approval on his kindly face. Thank God, there are some people left living who are not shamed to behold the symptoms of real love. John finally broke away and the two got the old Ford from the garage and drove away to the quarter that seems, always, to contain more than its share of misery, disease and pale death. But John was soon to know, as you shall now, how wise the old Romans actually were. The great Latin poet strummed his lyre while he sang: *"Pallido mors aequo pulsat pede pauperum tabernas, regnumque turres."* (Pale death that stocks with equal speed both the hovels of the poor, and the palaces of kings.')

Perhaps Virgil described the Stock Yards district of Chicago, more appropriately: *"Pallentesque habitant Morbi, tristrisque Senectus Et Metus, et malasuada Fames, et turpis Egastas."* ("Here dwells Pale Disease, and sad Old Age, and Fear, and Famine that drives to sin, and Ghastly Want.") No more apt description, made over 20 centuries ago, than John saw that afternoon.

As they drove slowly away from the doctor's residence, he brought up the matter of the proper marital adjustments, if marriage was to be, not hate. "John, my son," he said, "a large proportion of all the divorces we view with horror, is due to the uncontrolled, bull-in-a-china shop attitude of the bridegroom from the moment he is at last alone with his bride. The sex urge is so strong and uncontrolled that the bride, who has never known man, is shocked, brutally hurt, disgusted with the man who had just promised before God to love and cherish her. She feels, and not unnaturally, that she is his chattel, a little better that a woman of the street. A paid, legalized mistress.

"I have talked to hundreds of husbands and wives and know what I say is true. Nearly all men marry women and have nothing to base their conduct on but the teachings of the saloon and the gutter. It's this way, Son."

He went step after step into intimate details which, if

humans were only human, would be taught to prospective mates as co-equal with the marriage ceremony. "Son, I just cannot understand it. We claim to be believers in a God of Love, and act like we worshipped Dionysius, the God of Lust. Every right woman who loves a certain man is anxious and eager to enter into the most intimate relations with the man she has chosen to be the father of her children. Sex is holy because God established two sexes and commanded them to multiply and populate. Promise me that you will enter into Holy Matrimony with my Emilie in full control of your sexual impulses. Believe me, if you do, and I am sure you will do this, all else you will encounter in a long life will be as nothing to your divine experiences. Mother has instructed Emilie in the duties and the ecstacies of matrimony, and you will not find the least prudery or false modesty in that fine woman."

John reached out his right hand and strongly pressed his new father's arm, saying: "I learned strong self-control in many ways, not the least of which is my training in *ju-jitsu*, fencing and *savate*. You need have no fear."

"Thanks, my son," declared Dr. Zollner. "And now let us again discuss tuberculosis pulmonitis. It is both a syndrome and a disease. It is mainly a series of symptoms (syndromes) of starvation and want. Lack of means of warmuth, lack of decent, nutritious food, lack of clean air and sunlight, lack of humanitarian love. Son, the day will come – may it be soon – when men will look back on us as barbarians. And of all the culpable, the medical profession stands first because, as Jesus said: 'To whom much is given, from him much will be demanded.' "

By this time Dr. Zollner had driven to the 47th Street section on Halstead. There, for the first time, John saw misery personified. The Mexican packing house laborers lived there quite largely in squalid two story hovels of unpainted wood. Carrion lay around about to pollute the air. A small stream called Turkey Creek, that carried the discharging latrine and toilet from the abbatoirs, was as putrid as a career politician's mind and soul. Men were out skimming the fat from the Turkey Creek sewers to be melted, supposedly purified and run into pure hog lard for culinary purposes. (Author: a matter of public record.) The circumambient atmosphere was literally one grand stench.

"Good God, how can the people stand it?" asked John.

"It's the best they can get on the wages they draw, not earn, because they earn three times what they draw."

John continued: "I suppose the Board of Health is ruled by the A.M.A.?"

"But naturally, and it is hard to say which is the most debased and vile, the A.M.A. or the B. of H."

They entered hovel after hovel, each almost an exact duplicate of every other one. People, children of the Lord God, living more like swine than humans. The difference being that swine got plenty of very nutritious food, while the people lived on beans, little cheese, little off-grade beef, plenty of chili peppers to disguise the whole. The odor from the cooking was little better than that from the sewer creek. In most of the hovels there was one or more slowly coughing their lungs away. All this and more while crooked public officials stole the city, county and state dry to dine and wine prostitutes and ward heelers.

Many of the patients could not afford doctor's fees, or even to get prescriptions filled when the doctor donated his services. Dr. Zollner, being a Homeopath-Eclectic devotee, carried his medicines with him and gave them freely. If all the blessings thrown at him by these poor people had been accumulated they would have made an edifice many times as high as the Tower of Babel.

After three busy hours they drove toward home discussing, in particular, tuberculosis, nothing more than a starvation syndrome that was preventable if the rascals who robbed the public and God would do their sworn duty.

(Author: This all happened many years ago, but do not think for amoment it is any different, in the gross, than it was when John saw it. There are nearly 6 million families living in the United States on family incomes of less than $1000.00 a year. The author has full documentation. And the USDA ships needed commodities all over God's footstool, free and cartage paid, to other rotten government officials who sell and pocket. What cut do they get in return?)

"You see, John, it is being proved in the Alps in Europe, by brilliant doctors, that sunlight – pure and unadulterated – will prevent and very often cure TB. Of course an ample diet must be supplied. Furthermore, it is a fact that workers in dolomite quarries that the sun shines on, do not get TB. Dr. Niels Finsen, Bernhardt, Rollier and others are proving the cure without shadow of doubt. Finsen uses artificial sunlight that very closely approximates natural sunlight. He has made marvelous cures of skin TB which is called Lupus, the wolf. To prevent and cure TB of any kind we must remember the great motto at the University at Locarno: 'When doctors fail you, try these three – Dr. Diet, Dr. Quiet, Dr. Serenity.' Never forget, John, TB is nothing but the syndromes of starvation, and this will absolutely be proved before very many years. Especially when the medical trust gets out of political chicanery, and follows the footsteps of that Great Physician, Hippocrates, the father of honest medicine."

(Author: How true was the doctor's prophecy. Morris Fishbein, late czar of the A.M.A. collected a large amount of evidence about TB in Chicago. It was not startling; it was absolutely horrifying. He used the evidence of far better doctors who knew that the death rate among negroes in the north is the highest on record. That the death rate among Chicago Mexicans is eleven times the average rate of all citizens. The same thing holds true in nearly all large cities in the richest country on earth – the country that has hyperopia that can see a rheumatic louse in India and rush aid to it, but very conveniently passes over starving human beings right under its very nose.)

That same evening the family was sitting before a cannel coal fire in the parlor planning and discussing John's future as a necessary member of the family. John and Emilie were sitting on one of those old fashioned 'love seats' that barely permitted two people to sit without one sitting on the other's lap. He was holding her hands, although there was no possible reason why, for she would never strike him.

The telephone rang long and loud. Dr. Zollner answered it promptly and held quite an excited conversation. He was quite agitated as he began pulling on his coat. "John, as you practice medicine, you are going to see many heart-rending scenes. One of my classmates has just attempted suicide, and he is dying. He is begging me to come and, although his medical practice life has not been Godly or ethical, nevertheless, he is a human being, and as such we must offer him any help in our power. Will you go?"

John was on his feet before the doctor had finished his conversation because he remembered a wise saying of Dr. Pressing: "The doctor hears our first baby cries and our last dying groan. Between those two poles he must be able to offer every material and spiritual consolation." Good old Dr. Pressing!

The two men drove up Boule Miche some three miles and turned west to a long row of brick flats, sandstone trimmed. They halted at a three-story residence of an earlier vintage, and stopped. They entered and a colored butler took their wraps.

"How is the doctor now?" asked Dr. Zollner.

"I think he is mighty pooley, Suh," replied the butler. "In fact, Doctah, he thinks he will die tonight. He will not permit me to call any doctah but you, Suh. Will you step this way, please Doctah?"

They mounted a long, wide stairway with carpeting so deep it was like walking in deep snow. On entering the bed chamber, John saw a man of about fifty-five years lying partially undressed on a magnificent imported bed. He was weak and exsanguinated to the Nth degree. He was conscious, however, and weakly motioned for his visitors to come close to his bedside and seat themselves. His voice, although not much louder than a whisper, was plain and distinct.

"I have sent for you, Emil, because of our old friendship, before I became a great A.M.A. disciple, and then into this business of splitting fees, kickbacks, and all that.

"I have been, as every doctor knows, for a number of years, an abortionist, and have accumulated a large fortune." He stopped a short time to regain his breath, then continued: "A man from Arizona, whom they call Gullible Gus, the man who rediscovered the Lost Dutchman mine, was defrauded by several doctors, and out of vengeance, has affiliated himself with a number of honest doctors who do not worship at the shrine of such men as Simmons and Fishbein, swearing they will never cease trying to break up the medical monopoly, and make medicine the friend of man, not the enemy. Gullible Gus is all right. I am dying by my own hand. I now see clearly the hundreds of crimes I have committed. I've tried to fool myself into the belief in Atheism. I am about to stand before a higher court than the American Medical Association." The effort of speaking seemed to exhaust him almost to the ending, but he held on by sheer will power to that silver cord that binds the material man to the spiritual man. For five minutes he lay there gasping for breath and, with great effort, continued: "Emil, you were always of a spiritual mind – strange that Homeos are more so than Allopaths – will you pray for my guilty soul *now,* while there is time?" His pleading eyes reminded John of a dog he had had before the great tragedy in his life. There is nothing in heaven, or on earth more appealing than the eyes of a dog. John felt the tears about to overflow the lids, and wiped them away.

Dr. Zollner took his dying colleague by the hand and asked: "Fred, are you truly sorry for the misdeeds of your life, or are you merely frightened by the thought that you are passing into an unknown situation?"

"I am indeed sorry; frightened too, for the medical crimes I have committed must be almost unpardonable. But pray,

Emil."

"If you are truly repentant, Fred, you need have not the least fear. Jesus Christ pardoned the erring woman. He pardoned the thief, who was crucified with him. The Bible tells us that 'He that calleth on the name of the Lord shall be saved.' "

A quiver raced through the dying man's body and, for a moment, the doctor thought he was dead. He faintly opened his eyes and whispered: "Pray."

Dr. Zollner said in a firm voice: "Fred, let your last thought be, 'God have mercy on my soul.' And he will have mercy on your soul."

"Pray!" gasped the dying man.

Dr. Zollner firmly grasped the suppliant's hands as he prayed:

"Great Spirit, who sees the sparrow's fall, and who turns no repentant man away, look down on the spirit that is departing from the old clay shell. Forgive him in the name of Christ, and Thy never-ending Love for all of Thy creatures."

The dying doctor struggled a bit, raised his head and let it fall to the pillow. His lips could be seen forming the unspoken words: "God have mercy......on......"

Dr. Zollner took a pulse that no longer beat, and without loosing his grip on the dead man's hands, continued: "Heavenly Father, I do thank you for letting my son be present, that he may know and never forget that 'What doth it profit a man if he gain the whole world and lose his own soul?' Amen."

As the doctor and John drove slowly home, John asked: "What will happen to that poor man's spirit? Of course, no sensible man believes in a literal hell nowdays. Such a belief, to my mind, seems illogical, almost blasphemous. Even our Constitution forbids cruel and unusual punishment regardless of the crime. Furthermore, only material, tangible substances can be burned. I remember reading in the Bible, a long time ago: 'Then will the body return to the dust, and the Spirit to God who gave it.' Can Spirit be burned, Father Zollner?"

"No, my son," said the doctor as he looked fondly at his newly acquired son, "there is no hell except in orthodox religions. The mind, which is the real man, goes right on living. Death does not confer a golden harp, crown, slippers, wings, and the other fashionable accessories. Nor does the spirit of an unrepentant man find horns on his head, batwings on his shoulders, a harpoon instead of a harp, and a long barb-tipped prehensile tail.

"The modern concept is that the super-conscious mind, which is the Spirit, brings to the consciousness of the newborn spirit, every wrong that the person did in the material life. The conscience, which some think is the super-conscious, is polished up and vitalized until the mental sufferings of that soul are hotter than a hundred hells. Our late departed friend is now in good hands. He will have to go thorough a rather severe schooling before he is admitted to the lives of the blessed. You see, my son, there are so many apparent contradictions in our Bible, although only a fool would deny that it is, on the whole, divine. A person who looks up the life of Jesus Christ and denies Him Divinity, is a moron, because, if His teachings were followed, this world would not be a real hell. Shakespeare put it this way: 'Hell is empty. All the devils are here.' "

They drove along for a time, each busy with his own thoughts.

"You see, my son, no man can ever be lost. Jesus said: '*I will draw all men to me.*' Again: 'If you forgive men their trespasses, your heavenly Father will forgive you.' "

"But why the contradictions?" asked John.

"Because every language has its idioms which are not entirely, if ever, fully understood by translators," said the doctor. "Tens of millions of humans have been slaughtered over such questions as 'free will', 'grace', 'pre-destination', 'trans-substantiation', 'the immaculate conception', the assumption of Mary into heaven without undergoing death', which is in itself nothing but birth into the very center of immortality. As an example of how errors occur, let us take the Latin verb, *SUMO*. It means almost anything, and nothing. In English 'sumo' means, 'to take, lay hold of, assume, get, receive, borrow, bestow, choose, employ, undertake, use, take for granted, demand, cite, mention, lie with, buy,' *et cet., ad infinitum.*

"Now, that is but one example of thousands of words in hundreds of languages. Even our own language is pretty inaccurate even with us who use it. For example the word 'observe' means to see, or to say. Apprehend means to fear, or understand, or arrest by officers. Have I made the matter clear, son? Just two examples among thousands."

When they reached home, for this was to be John's home from then on, they found a substantial supper awaiting them. Then they adjourned to the best parlor to discuss the whole situation. It was decided that John and Emilie should be married as soon as possible, and that John should stay in Chicago and finish his pre-medic and his medical course there. The death of the doctor John had seen, had somewhat depressed him for it seemed almost inconceivable that one who had taken the sacred Oath of Hippocrates should take lives instead of doing his very best to save lives. About 10 P.M. the ladies retired, leaving Dr. Zollner and John in a position to discuss medical subjects that might not be of great interest to the women folks.

Dr. Zollner smoked his large meerschaum, blew rings toward the high ceiling and watched them fade into nothingness. And yet, he knew that nothing was lost, for solids had only turned into an equal amount of gases floating in the air – gases that would in turn be converted into solids through photosynthesis. It was true of common water; it freezes into a hard, solid body; returning to a liquid when warmed. If warmed still more, it is converted into invisible steam, only to return to liquid water again by condensation. Absolutely nothing was lost. Nothing ever would be lost. If mother always forgives an erring son, was God less than a human mother? He blew a large ring to the ceiling and remarked: "Son, you are worried about the future of the man we just saw die. Be assured that this poor, spiritually ignorant person is in far better hands that you can imagine.

"The Book tells us, common reason tells us, that the Latins spoke truly: '*De nihilo nihil, in nihilum nil posse reverti.*' Do you understand its meaning?"

"I'd say it means nothing can be made from nothing, and nothing existing can be reduced to nothing," replied John.

"Fine, my son, and now let us study the supernatural for a change. Right in this great city one may find persons crooked as the serpents that Moses metamorphosed from his staff. I am speaking of mediums who have made a mockery of a God-given faculty, just exactly as did the poor fellow we saw as he was dying. He had turned the blessed art of healing into a money making racket.

"On the contrary, there are honest mediums, just as there are many honest physicians. And some of these mediums are just as much inspired as any you will find in the Bible. You remember that woman of Endor who was able to cause the materialization of the High Priest Samuel? There are mediums who, given the right conditions, can put you in communication with friends and folks who have passed into life eternal. I have experienced that communication. Let me say in all truth that no truth-seeking scientist, clergyman, jurist, or layman has ever investigated the subject without accepting the creed of survival, and communication with the so-called 'dead'."

He paused long enough to let John interject a question that has puzzled men since the time of the Prophets.

"Why are mediums neccessary?"

"You cannot talk to your family right now. But, if you go to the telephone, you use the instrument as a medium. Another medium, the operator, takes your call. She calls another medium at your home town, and she uses another medium (telephone) to ring your folks. They in turn must use another medium, their phone before you can communicate. It's just as easy, as logical and as true as that."

"Why must these mediums have darkness to put you in touch with the infinite?"

"My son, they do not need darkness except in case of the actual materialization of spirits, who are thus able to take on the lost physical semblance from ectoplasm furnished by the medium. Light injures ectoplasm demonstrations just as light affects the film used in making pictures. You have been reading about this new thing called radio. You probably have heard the messages received over long distances. It is a positive fact that radio reception is far, far better when it is dark. I repeat that every scientist, minister, many great rulers, have proved the fact of survival and spirit communication under circumstances and conditions that absolutely rule out any possible trickery or chicanery. I wish I could report with equal favor on the medical societies and the men who rule nearly every doctor with a rawhide scourge. Or on a million rascals in government."

John started to reply but the ringing of the telephone bell interrupted him. Dr. Zollner answered the call and talked earnestly for some time. He made an appointment with an X-ray technician to be consummated at the Billings Hospital.

"There's another one of those new gadgets for scientific medicine to play with, and charge like hades," snorted the doctor. "This party definitely has X-ray cancer on both hands. The surgeon insists on a double amputation. I favor the new technique of several great European doctors — electro-coagulation. But much surgery nowadays is nothing but a racket, just plain stealing. One might think that there would be no such chicanery amongst doctors, but it is disgraceful to see the jealousy, the hatred, the back biting in a noble profession. Why is this? Just plain *fear,* my son. Many physicians who have been caught red-handed in criminal, or ignorant mal-practice, long to get something on every other doctor as a matter of self defense, meantime the patients suffer, and die."

"What are the dangers in using X-rays?" asked John.

"That is difficult to say although it has been observed and proved that any type of radiation shorter than the solar rays to which man has been acclimated to for whole eons, tends to produce cancer. I am not a prophet, or the son of a prophet, but I do prophesy from the bottom of all the reasoning power I possess that the day is not distant when X-rays will be used in diagnosis and treatment to a far greater amount than is safe or sane. As of now, it is difficult to see the end of it all. But I see disaster ahead for the human race from radiation of shorter wave length than one finds in the sun. In fact it has been established that even solar rays under certain conditions have instituted skin cancers."

(Author: Dr. Zollner was a true phophet. The number of X-ray cancers on the hands of dentists, who have used the killer rays in examining human jaws, is horrifying. Today commercialized medicine is demanding that every child be X-rayed twice a year to detect latent TB, with the natural resultant of greatly increased cancer rate. Tuberculin is safer, better in every way. Van Dellen, another doctor with a flair for authorship, has pointed out the horrific fact that X-rays are the potent cause of the increase in leukemia which is cancer of the blood cells. One wonders if the gentleman ever looks back over his screeds of the past. He stated, in the columns of 'The World's Greatest Newspaper' that the children of those that worked with X-rays were nine times as liable to have leukemia – an incurable disease – as the offspring of doctors that do not work with the killer rays. Van Dellen, a bright and shining star in the A.M.A. firmament, has stated these things many times, but still advises the use of the X-rays. The consensus of the opinions of really honest physicians, some of whom still are tied to the A.M.A. apron strings, and yet cannot completely cast aside their voluntary Hippocratic Oath, unequivocally and positively condemn the use of X-rays and radium in the treatment of cancer, the disease that bids fair to run us all down the drain.

* * * * *

One of the most highly regarded oncologists (cancer specialists) said not long ago that cancer surgery was the greatest graft the medical profession had ever enjoyed. A young doctor in Kansas City has gotten wealthy before he has reached the age of 43 by practicing suspected cancer surgery. He watches carefully, you might say diabolically, the graduates from medical colleges. He worms his slimy coils into their confidence, and when the time is ripe, he persuades them to throw all their surgical cases his way for the usual price of betrayal and treason to the once noble art of healing by drugs and other media used by medical doctors.

He recently stated: "I went into surgery to make a fortune quickly. I make more in two hours than a general practicioner can possibly earn in two weeks of hard work including night calls." Small wonder that those who know the facts of life are wont to speak of surgery as sadism. In 1957, a Dr. Smith, a physician of enormous practice in both medicine and surgery, a man who had great experience in the study of tumors, recently stated in Los Angeles: *"America has the best doctors, the best medical schools, the best hospitals in the world. Nevertheless, I do not know a well person. In the last year we have had more deaths from cancer, hypertension, cerebral hemorrhage, diabetes, heart disease, and other degenerative diseases than any year in our history."*

The future Dr. John Marsh Pressing is going to know why that is, and so will all of us, as we follow his career in honest, conscientious healing, employing everything that heals. And all of us will learn of the horrifying conditions in fire trap – not fire proof – hospitals. And why so many doctors have to resort to gadgetry to attempt to make diagnoses – admittedly poor medical training, if we may possibly believe governmental doctors.)

CHAPTER 10

Who knows a truth and a falsehood tells,
My soul abhors him like a thousand hells. – Homer

After much consulation with Dr. and Mother Zollner, John and Emilie came to a difinite understanding about all the possible road blocks to a happy marriage. From long experience Dr. Zollner knew that sex was the main impediment in that state of bliss. He said, and truthfully: "The ignorant bull-in-a-china-shop attitude of a bridegroom, during the so-called honeymoon, is the main factor in turning the honey into vinegar. That far too often, the first night of marriage plants the seed that ends in divorces, ill health, and even suicide and murder." After a thorough examination, including Wasserman tests, the day was set as of December 25th – Christmas Day.

It was a simple home wedding with only the nearest relatives and friends as invited guests. Of course Dr. Pressing and Mom were present. It would have been unthinkable to see a dear son, although an adopted son, enter into the most important contract and sacrament of his life were they not present. There was no ignorant display or fanfare, things that start a bride off tired to extinction. It was Christmas vacation, so John and his bride drove a good used Ford up into Wisconsin to a lodge a friend of the Zollner family kindly placed at the disposal of the newlyweds.

On their return to Chicago, John re-entered pre-med and Emilie began a course in practical nursing, determined to be a real helpmate to her John. A single glance at the couple was enough to assure any critic they had made the proper adjustments presaging a really happy and successful marriage. They radiated happiness and contentment.

(Author: Will someone who knows please tell us why young girls are permitted to marry without the least possible knowledge or instruction in the duties as well as the felicities of married life? Why wait until there is discord, mental agony, sometimes actual abhorrence before seeking advice? In time to come, the future will condemn this generation as barbarians. Poor adjustments lead to hatred, divorce, children almost sure to turn out as delinquents. Let it be understood right now that every adjustment had been made by John and his bride for there was a full intellectual, spiritual and sexual mating. The bridle that he had used for self control was paying off, and big.)

John's pre-med course was extremely easy, for Dr. Zollner was a lexicon of medicine, literature and contemporary art. As John accompanied him on hundreds of calls, the doctor put him through a course of pre-med that no college could offer. It can be truthfully affirmed that, already being a gentleman, his character was neither changed for worse, nor better. He was a gentleman born, possibly a throwback from before his own stormy parents. Perhaps they would not have been so stormy if medical racketeers had not slashed and burned her poor physical body until every semblance of femininity was erased from her. A human suffering intense pain for a long term of years can hardly escape form nerves.

Nowadays, some young brides are so very anxious to have a menagé of their own that they nag their grooms until he goes head over heels into debt for a house – not necessarily a home – and furnishes it with modern garish, short-lived furniture. "The show's the thing," they think. John and Emilie lived and worked and loved with the Zollner family. And meantime John was getting an education that no college or university could offer. He and Emilie lived with her family, which was John's family now, and John insisted on paying their share of the household expenses, for he had not yet begun to go deeply into the insurance money his mother had left him. Furthermore, he knew that his other Dad and Mom had made him the sole beneficiary of their estate, which, although not a great sum in these decadent times, nevertheless, was, as Dr. Pressing said: 'Nothing to sneeze at.'

The following fall, John entered a regular medical school, one of the Windy City's best and most reputable, because the founder had been a man of the commodity so much needed by doctors, namely common sense. Or as he once expressed it when he spoke of flamboyant and uppish medicine men as: "Not having sense that God gave geese."

This is what Dr. Benjamin Rush said, and he meant every word: "Remember how many of our most useful remedies have been discovered by quacks. Do not be afraid of conversing with them, and by profiting through their ignorance and temerity."

(Author: Ignorance? Temerity? A great internist, a highly reputable doctor, said: "Out of every 100 operated cases, at least 60% are proved an incorrect diagnosis." Why did the surgeon general liken most doctors to plumbers? Why did another surgeon general say: "Medical colleges do not teach medical students real diagnosis?" Why is it necessary, if medical science *is* a science, to send over half the sick folks to hospitals? What will compare with the doctor's several physical senses? He may employ, more or less ignorantly and uselessly, a multitude of gadgets. But in the end he positively has to use his fingers, ears, eyes and nose.

Here is something else Dr. Rush wrote:

"The practice of physic (medicine) has been more improved by the casual experimenter of illiterate nations, and the rash ones of vagabond quacks, than all of the once celebrated professors of it, and the theoretic teachers in the several schools (medical) in Europe, very few of whom have furnished us with one new medicine, or have taught us better to use our old ones, have in any instance at all, improved the art of curing disease."

By the time John's first year in medical college was over, he had more histology, anatomy, bacteriology, urology, neurology, materia medica and gynecology, not to speak of anaesthesiology and surgery than any three members of the freshly graduated class. And why not? He was born to be a healer and his entire life since the death of his blood parents had been medicine in all its phases. Dr. Zollner had taken his medicine at the best Germany and Austria had to offer in the way of training and he passed his accumulated knowledge on to his new son as they visited the sick, on their way to and from, and as they sat before the heart-warming cannel coal fire that blazed in the grate.

Nearing the end of his first year in medical college, he often heard students speak of cigarettes as 'coffin nails', and wondered why. The cigarette manufactures were advertising widely and vociferously their arsenic loaded smokes. Then John noted that many smokers were establishing themselves with a curious cough, dry in some, wet in others. When they ceased smoking for a time, the cough left, that is if they had been light smokers. Those who smoked constantly and tried to taper off became ill indeed. The cough did not subside even when they quit entirely. He noticed, too, that these constant smokers panted when they walked rapidly or mounted the stairs at the college. He began to get the suspicion that these drug addicts were spelling disaster to themselves concerning the heart, and he wondered if that cigarette cough might not be incipent cancer of the mouth, throat or lungs. He found a known case of mouth cancer caused by the hot bit of an old pipe, took some of the tissue and examined it in the bacteriology laboratory. Two of the students who coughed badly readily permitted him to swab their throats, and that, too, John put under the low, and then the high power of a microscope. There was a definite similarity between the cellular tissue from a cancerous lip and the material from the throats.

What to do? Should he tell his suspicions to the docent in bacteriology? Should he tell the students? He finally passed his finding on to Father Zollner and asked his opinion and advice. The doctor confirmed that belief by some recent medical journals from Europe and advised John to take the matter up with his bacteriology and histology professor. That worthy, a disciple of Maurice Fishbein, laughed at John's findings and told him to forget it. In fact the prof was just a bit nasty.

(Author: Those two students finally became too ill to continue their medical course. They were hospitalized and some of the best-rated, not necessarily the best, doctors in Chicago studied the cases and differed, as far as the north pole is from the south pole, in their diagnosis. If medicine is a science, they should have agreed, because the word science is derived from the Latin verb "scire" meaning "to know." In short the two students died with what could have been nothing less than bronchogenic cancer. The cause – the irritation from CO, tar, pyridins and insecticide residual – *arsenic*. John assured himself of the fact by obtaining portions of their lungs and checking for arsenic with the Marsh test.)

Let us step ahead to the year 1950. Cigarette cancer had been by this time killing 11,000 to 25,000 per annum, and growing worse all the time. Year after year more and more people were dying from lung cancer and in direct ratio to the increase in the sales of cigarettes. The best oncologists (cancer specialists) were thundering their blasts at these cigarettes. Cigarette manufacturers then began hiring movie queens, ball players, society women to recommend cigarettes. Cigarette manufactures then began hiring scoundrels calling themselves doctors to make faked tests and make faked reports such as: "no evidence that cigarettes cause cancer."

In 1952, Dr. Graham of St. Louis, a tumor specialist, began a long series of tests on the carcenogenic effects of cigarette smoking. He stated there was absolutely no doubt that cigarettes caused cancer, and had a deleterious effect on the heart. About the same time, the Journal of the A.M.A. ran a lead by Ochsner, another cancer specialist, stating there could not be the least doubt that cigarette smoking caused lung cancer. *In the same issue of that same Journal there were two full-page ads for cigarettes! Talk about hypocrisy!*

Back in 1933, several chemists and physicians proved there

were arsenical residents in cigarette tobacco. They proved, and the A.M.A. Journal will have to admit it, that arsenic causes cancer. The above reports are matters of public record and anybody can easily verify all of this. Even the A.M.A. Journal has at times reported the dangers of cigarettes to lungs, heart and brain. *But,* these comments are only published in a commercialized Journal that goes to doctors so the public never sees them. Why doesn't the A.M.A. give press releases showing the hazards in cigarettes, DDT, arsenic insecticides, dieldrin, parathion, and a thousand other extremely poisonous coal tar substances found in everything man eats and drinks, and in the air?

The World's Greatest Newspaper (?) carried Van Dellen's medical column, November 27th, 1957, stating the highly watered down data concerning smoking, drinking, cancer. He quoted the results recorded by Dr. D. A. Sandowsky, who had studied 2500 cases in government hospitals, and found that smoking tobacco in any form was the prime cause of cancer in mouth, throat and lungs. Lip cancer by cause of cancer in mouth, throat and lungs. Lip cancer caused by pipe smoking. Tongue and mouth cancers from cigar smoking.

Then Van Dellen, who has a real flair for writing medical topics and overlooking the defalcations of organized greed in medicine, reported on the findings of Drs. Wynder and Bross of the Sloan-Kettering institute. They apparently proved that the smoking of tobacco, well larded with insecticides, as well as the drinking of raw whiskey, were the *bete noir* in cancers of the respiratory tract and the gastro-intestinal tract. They left no doubt in any sane man's mind that cigarettes and raw alcoholic drinks do cause cancer.

That very same day the World's Greatest Newspaper ran many ads for whiskey and cigarettes. Just how rotten can men become in the mad race for the almighty dollar?

Now two queries: Larrick, of the F.D.A., why do you not place placards in every post office warning all that cigarettes and whiskey cause cancer? What kind of a human being are you? You *permit* the distribution of cancer causes, while you *castigate* cancer cures.

Shakespeare says it so well: "Thus Judas did to Christ, who in twelve found truth in all but one. I in twelve thousand, none." Was Shakespeare psychic? Did he, by prescience, see a great nation in the West going down the drain because of prostituted politicians? Did he foresee the additives to foods such as coal tar derivatives, hormones, arsenic, lead, copper, manganese, selenium (the worst of all insecticidal poisons)? Did he glance ahead three centuries and find the water polluted with one of the worst of poisons – fluorine? Did he see the fact that the Communists applaud this addition because it weakens men's wills to be free? Whether he did, or did not, it has all come true. Nero fiddled while Rome burned. Modern rulers golf, fish, vacation four days out of every week, while America marches on to disaster.

When are *you* going to wake up and assume your just rights under the glorious Constitution? When are you going to run putrid politicians out of soft sinecures into nice, high, thick masonry walls such as we find at Atlanta, Leavenworth and that little, well-known island just off California? Benedict Arnold was a saint compared with some parties we could honestly name. Oh! the sadness and the horror of it when the food poisoners and the Borgias load even tobacco with fatal, long-enduring poisons. And shame to a government that lets them get away with it!

Executive Department, did you not know that radioactive strontium has increased 300% in two years in the Valley? Did you know that some apple orchards, near Washington, have accumulated up to 134 pounds of DDT per acre? Do you know that Texas Research, a non-profit research organization, proved that DDT is taken up by growing plants for the live stock and those of us the USDA considers the lesser, to eat and assimilate this cumulative coal-tar-synthetic devil's dusting powder?

Why do we not all write the President, our every member of Congress, demanding, as we have every right to demand, that these wrongs be rectified? Why not demand that Bricker of Ohio be investigated and thrown out from the sacred halls of Congress? This writer has been battling with Washington for years and has some most remarkable replies — safely concealed, I promise you.

My ancestors came over in the Mayflower, and the Ark and Dove. I am a free-born American citizen, and bear wounds on my body to prove my loyalty. Yet I went through veritable persecution at the hands of many of the officials of the A.M.A. and the Wisconsin Alumni Research Foundation, who conspired to steal my private papers and steal my inventions for the photosynthesis of vitamin D. And, believing, as I do, not only in my citizen's rights, but that one cannot die, I say: "Do your worst. If I can only get this great sleeping giant, the People, to arise and throw *you* scoundrels out, as Jesus threw your kind from the Temple of the Lord, it will be worth any price." I have before me as I write, over a thousand reports on cigarette cancers, all made by reputable physicians whose honor has not been for sale, stating that there is absolutely no doubt that smoking causes cancer. Furthermore, the records show that 32 million Americans suffer from incurable hypertension. The same records show that the smoking of one cigarette causes a raise of as high as 34 points in blood pressure. Those records come from Van Dellen's own column in The Chicago Tribune. Assume a boiler built to sustain a steam pressure of 150 pounds. The fireman ties down the safety valve and up goes the boiler, and the fireman. Now then, assume that your B.P. stands at 170 mm. You smoke a coffin nail and it jumps up 34 points to 204. There is an even chance that a blood vessel in the brain bursts, and you are lucky if you never come to, for cerebral palsy and "stroke" turns most men into driveling, helpless zombies. Let any man deny these statements and I will drive the lie down his mendacious mouth.

I stand ready and more than willing to produce the documents that will prove every statement I have ever made, ever will make. I declare again that America is being betrayed by the politicians and doctors we pay to protect us. Tell us, Washington, why the Russians beat us at every stage of the game? What is Dulles doing for America? Tell us about Stassen and his perpetual give-away. Tell us what we have handed over to Britain just because Her Majesty visited us? What happened when her father stopped and stayed at the White House? And what about the man, who after King George returned, gave us his siren song that goes something like this: "My friends, I tell you again, and again, that your sons are not going to be sent abroad to die on foreign battle fields." Remember? How many mothers gave boys to die on foreign battle fields during the following few years? How many died in World War II? How many hundred billions of once good American dollars are today sustaining and giving comfort to foreign governments?)

* * *

John had made such wonderful progress, and so easily, that at the end of the first year the Board of Regents permitted him to take a written and oral examination that placed him one year ahead of schedule, that is in the Junior class. Not only that, John was filling in as docent when some professors were necessarily absent from their classes.

One thing above all sickened and disgusted John — that was the bestial abuse of the remains of one who once lived, in an attempt to "harden themselves in." No wild beasts in a Roman arena ever treated human remains with such abject beastiality as did some of these medical students. Nor will you be shocked with a relation of these orgies in human flesh. One more thing aroused his just ire — the brutality used in live animal vivisection to prove nothing of value. Some of the animals were human.

John learned much concerning this most brutal and brutalizing practice of many doctors of medicine. First, they stated that the humans, or the other animals were given pain killing drugs.

(Author: Hell spawned that lie. Visit a vivisection laboratory and discover for yourself, if you have the intestinal fortitude, that the torture inflicted on man's only friends through the ages, dogs, make a human crucifixion seem like a Sunday School picnic. Watch but one dog, whose abdomen has been slit open, and then certain veins or arteries tied off until parts of the tortured dog, perhaps some child's pet, rot and drop off. In the meantime the dog is not given water. This is but one of the minor degradations that supposed humans do to our lesser brothers. "God is not mocked," says the Book – but of course this kind of human ghouls do not believe in God. God made all creatures. He made the same convenant with animals that he made with Noah. Animals (Revelation 5:13) will stand before the seat of power and worship our common God. Will that same God who notes the fall of a sparrow, hold man guiltless for his supreme tortures of the lesser brothers that He placed under man's dominion and care?

British medical journals recently condemned the use of humans in vivisection. Dr. Thedford Taylor, who presided at the Nuremburg torture trials, stated categorically that the use of hundreds of thousands of human beings in torture vivisection tests had not added one iota to the sum total of medical knowledge. In the face of the statement, let the medical monopolies tell us what can be learned by torturing dogs? Is it not a fact that those S.S. Nazi doctors of medicine and murder started their careers of crime on man's only real friends, dogs? Did they not next start their fiendish animal experiments of captured humans, first employing pain preventing drugs, and after that slashing their captive Jews into shreds without anesthetics to prove not a thing, according to General Taylor?

The modern A.M.A. technique in treating cancer is nothsurgeons admit this truth. Hundreds of reputable physicians, and thank God there are thousands, condemn vivi-

ing more or less than human vivisection, and the very best sectors and vivisection in the most bitter terms. In fact one noted cancer specialist recently said of any doctor that experimented on animals: "Vivisection is hell. And I would not trust one of those sons of Hades in a sick room."

CHAPTER 11

GIVE THE SAP A STONE!

"Modern bread will not support a rat in health." Lessing, Cumberbatch, and hundreds of other reputable biologists.

John knew a lot more about psychosomatics than the doctor who invented the name. Let no man assume that John Marsh Pressing was anything less than a real he man. No man, however big, tough or strong could put anything across on him or on a weaker man, if John saw it. On a short visit he and Emilie made to see Doctor and Mother Pressing, while they were waiting at the station to catch a train home, a large, powerful man, a true bully, came to the station and began slapping a man not half his bulk and cursing him. The man, realizing he was no match for this tormentor, cried and pleaded like a young child. The bully, a section foreman on the railroad, seemed to think it great sport – and perhaps it was, to him.

John watched for a few minutes, his indignation temperature rising like the mercury in a thermometer in the mouth of a malaria patient. It reached the stage where he just could not see this dastardly thing. The foreman easily outweighed John by 60 pounds. John put down his valise and walked over to the bully and the bullyee and remarked, without raising his voice: "Stranger, I do not know what this is all about, nor do I care. You stop abusing that man right this instant."

The bully looked disdainfully at John and snorted: "What do you aim to do about it, country boy?"

"I said that you should not abuse a man half your size. Touch him again and find out what I will do about it."

The man evidently thought he had better tend to John and then finish off the small man. He drew back his ham-like fist and launched it at John. His weight carried him forward as John dodged a pile-driver blow. John turned his back, caught the bully by the wrist and threw the man neatly over his head. The man fell like a log or hog and lay still. John walked over and took his pulse. Then he drew some water in a convenient pail and sloshed it over his late antagonist, who came to sputtering like an old Ford model T engine in zero weather.

John walked over to the small man and asked the cause of the difficulty. The man had been working on the bully's section and had only asked for the money due him. He only wanted to spend the week end at his home in Steinmetz. He said: "Mr. Brillings has my pay check in his pocket right now and will not give it to me because he thinks I will not come back."

"Were you expecting to take the same train we are waiting for?" asked John.

"I was, but I have no money."

John walked over to the bully who, although he had regained his feet, was weaving in the breeze like a lily, which he was not. "Give this man his pay check," he ordered.

The man got his check without an instant's delay.

"Brillings," said John, "my name is Pressing. Son of Dr. Pressing. I intend to take up your infernal bullying with the division superintendent. I think you will be looking for another job."

Emilie had watched the proceeding with the light of love, joy, vast approval and war in her eyes. When they were safely seated in a chair car, she patted him on the free hand and said: "Good boy. The father of another I hope will be just like him."

John was astounded and showed it as he turned his best medical gaze on his wife. "Emilie, darling, what have you been holding out on me?"

" I thought good doctors knew everything," she smiled saucily. "But you have one guess."

John felt like doing a somewhat unethical thing by embracing a beautiful woman in a chair car. But he laid that aside until they were safely in their home with Dr. and

Mother Zollner. I would not tell you that he did not do considerable hand holding and patting on convenient portions of her anatomy. If I did I might be as great a liar as the University Foundation that called itself an eleemosynary institution, and robbed sick babies. Not to even mentioning the filching of another man's invention for the photosynthesis of vitamin D. And then demanded and received a release from paying income taxes, claiming to be a charitable institution. Whom the shoe fits, wear it and like it. To the officers: did you pay income taxes on the lush incomes you drew on another man's invention? Remember what the U.S. Courts said about it. Remember what the Capital-Times said about it. Why are you not in gaol?

Now about those psychosomatic symptoms John occasionally had. We remember that he saw his mother shoot his father and then turn the gun on herself. You do not have to be a psychologist to know the awful imprint the scene left in John's superconscious. Emilie knew all about that and, better, she knew what to do, for as said the poet: "Men are only boys grown tall. Hearts don't change much after all." It was no unusual thing for John to go peacefully to sleep on hitting the bed. That is, if there were not more important matters to attend to. But often he woke up, bathed in cold perspiration, crying: "Mother don't shoot. For God's sake don't shoot Dad!"

Without speaking, Emilie slipped her arms under his head and drew it over on her lush, snow-white bosom, meantime, softly humming a little German cradle song her mother had sung to all her children when they had nightmares.

And now it seemed that John was going to have to forego that sweet privilege for what was to come. That night after the couple were in their suite on the second floor, he made a careful examination and confirmed the good news Emilie had conveyed to him on the train. There was one soft spot that John was going to lose before many moons had passed. As a matter of fact, after the baby came, the nightmares from which he had suffered became much lighter and at less frequent intervals. A new baby in a home proved a soverign remedy. No man, doctor or pleb, can burp a baby and ride a nightmare at the same time.

* * *

The medical college that John honored as a docent, a student and America's greatest doctor-to-be, had, at the time, medical aspirants from pretty well over the globe. Every race was represented, with their various colors and customs. John made it a point to mingle with all of them and in particular a student from Jamaica, who although as black as the ace of spades, was a top-side scholar. Ewing was, so to speak, an outcast because of his color. Being truly ambitious to be a specialist in tropical diseases, he gritted his teeth and took the cold shoulders of men who were in no way his equal. There were two more students that were great friends – the son of a Chinese mandarin who used the pseudonym, Ku, and a Parsee East Indian named Lal.

Ku was of the traditional yellowish color. Lal's color was hard to describe, brownish with an undercoating of purple. A high-caste Indian in every respect, educated to the Nth degree in India and England, now was finishing off in Chicago. Ewing, Ku and Lal were there for but one purpose – get all the healing knowledge known to man. They never took part in sports, the usual campus rowdyism, and never desecrated needlessly the cadavers they dissected to find just how man is put together physically. And Ku and Lal had jointly evolved a theory of what constituted the mind of man, for mind and brain are not at all the same thing.

Yes, despite our great Jefferson's noble epigram of equal birth and opportunity, so well expressed in the Constitution of the United States, these three representatives of the brown, the yellow and the black races were considered far from equal by all of the Caucasian race, with the one exception of John. A life-long brotherhood grew up between the four that exists to this day. Lal had already taken an Osteopathic degree in England and was attending a night school teaching Chiropractic while carrying on a pretty stiff course in medicine. These are the true Disciples of Hippocrates who will bring peace to the world, thought John and Dr. Zollner, who always welcomed three fine gentlemen at his home.

How little we Caucasians really think when we remember that the Hindoos and the Chinese were peoples of highest culture when our ancestors were eating our own kind in cannibalism. Strange as it may seem, Jewish students, who are Caucasian along with the Hindoos, were the least receptive and friendly to Ku and Lal.

(Author: And that sets the picture for some of the dastardly and cowardly behavior perpetrated by the slave drivers who bossed the A.M.A. A man named Palmer reasoned, after much study and observation, that many diseases were primarily due to "subluxations" in the spinal column and practiced his new science, Chiropractic, with good results. The A.M.A. oligarchy almost threw itself into fits as they derided "this fish monger", forgetting that the Great Physician chose his Disciples largely from fishers and members of the Jewish race, even as Fishbein was both Jew and persecutor.

In the meantime, Dr. Sill established his school of Osteopathy, and often healed completely after orthodox medicine had failed. And a Jewish doctor, Abrams had advanced his Spondylotherapy, which is basically nothing less than Chiropractic as practiced today. The A.M.A. was very happy about the Abrams matter until he brought forth a new concept in healing employing his Oscilloclast. Then off went the A.M.A. roof, leading to some of the most damnable persecution that commercial corporation ever inflicted on a Doctor of Medicine. As Dr. Abrams knew first hand some of the rascality of the medical corporation, he attempted to guard the mechanism of his

Oscilloclast by sealing it up in a case, and every purchaser agreed in writing never to open the case under any circumstances. The A.M.A. took the same attitude it has taken toward known cancer cures such as those of Hoxsey, Lincoln, Drosnes-Lazenby, Koch et cet. Someone (guess who) actually stole the instruments, took them to the *Scientific American* and had that publication make X-rays of Abrams' Oscilloclast.

The radiographs showed there were no direct connections made by wiring inside the Oscilloclast and, as one who knows the inner workings of the gigantic racket knows, the Oscilloclast was declared a fraud. No wired connections! Didn't those experts ever hear of induction? They realized that unless Abrams was crushed, unless Chiropractic was crushed, the A.M.A. medicine men were going to take the beating of all time. Many leaders in medicine (names supplied) were using the Oscilloclast and getting results. But under the dire threats of the A.M.A. hierarchy they forgot their honor, their integrity and their sacred Oath, and ceased using the Oscilloclast. This is all ancient history now, but it is mentioned to show that the leopard never changes its spots.

Let those experts only look up the words induction and vibration, and apply them to their lost art of healing. They have even forced the Government to persecute distributors of the jury mast, a really great medical modality. Modern A.M.A. medicine simply seeks to limit the number of doctors, urging "shots" so one M.D. can do a day's work in two hours, and "damn the patients." Just the perpetuation of political physic. And I am not referring to the type of physic that you buy at the druggist shop for the purpose of causing the BM. How many A.M.A. drivers own stock in the companies selling hundreds of quack pills, potions, cosmetics, and the like? I personally know several of them, and the proof is handy.)

So our John became the fast friend of three future great doctors and often spent much time with them, as much as was possible considering the beautiful wife, the new heir, and his own course in medicine. He got much Confucian philosophy from Ku. But the Parsee, Dr. Lal had the most to confer on him; of Buddhism, of Chiropractic, of most ancient medicine practiced by the Hindoo healers centuries before the time of Luke the physician. There were times that some of the students had an itch to rough up the non-combatant Ku and Lal. These roughnecks had seen John in action on a few occasions, and one glance from his icy-blue eyes brought a change in intention, if not of heart.

The A.M.A. had agents circulating among the students proselyting future A.M.A. slaves. Slaves who would bend the knee and let the agents for the drug trust tell them how to practice medicine, through the supreme medical trust hierarchy. John soon learned that there was great value in Chiropractic, the hierarchy to the contrary notwithstanding.

One day, after a more than usual outburst of unrighteous wrath from Fishbein in the Journal, John had Dr. Lal up to take salt (and a lot of fine German cooking) with the family. A finer, more courteous gentleman never blessed the board of any Chicago residence. He taught the ladies how to wind many ells of silk into the Parsee turban, and showed them the ancient Hindoo method of knowing the present and forecasting the future.

After the ladies had retired, the three men drew up about the heart-warming cannel coal grate fire and discussed shop. Dr. Lal pointed out many cures effected, to his own knowledge, by Chiropractic manipulation in correcting subluxations. (Nota bene: the A.M.A. doctors castigated Palmer for many years for his reasoning about the disease conditioning by subluxations of segments of the vertebra. The A.M.A. denied categorically the existence of subluxations.)

Dr. Zollner said to John: "My son, get the medical lexicon." On receiving it he turned the pages and read from the best of medical works: "Spondylexartrosis – Luxation of vertebra."

(Author: Again the A.M.A. had been firing blanks. Let us ask the A.M.A. this question: Are the surgeons' latest graft, slipped disc fusions, anything else but surgery to correct a subluxation? And how about those coccygeal operations such as the coccygectomy? Why not own up that you opened your big mouth to condemn something you should know, but did not, and got your big brogans caught in it?)

Even Dr. Zollner had a skeleton in his closet – just an anatomical exhibit for study, and it was now brought forth while Dr. Lal pointed out possible pathology if certain vertebrae impinged certain nerves. Dr. Zollner, who had taken medicine in Europe, and later done post graduate work in Vienna, the then Mecca for American doctors, recounted his own personal experience while he was there. His principal interest was in the so-called 'jury mast' that permitted the stretching of the vertebral column so subluxed sections could be easily shifted into place without pain. This modality had been a great success until the medical monopoly had to condemn it in order to damn Dr. Palmer and his scientific Chiropractic.

(Author: Special to the A.M.A.: If you do not own a copy of Spears' little, but very informative journal, I will be glad to see that you get it. That hospital and sanitarium is doing, without surgery or blarney, what orthodox medicine has not been able to do since the A.M.A. took over and turned a once noble profession into you know what. Just take a look at the pictures in that little journal and see patients orthodox medicine had done nothing for, then see photos taken a short time later. You see patients come in with A.M.A. devised harnesses of torture, and in a few days or weeks see them with the devilish devices removed. As one who had a medical education, I must admit that these cures smack of the miracles under the gentle hands of the Great Physician. You should see the

the cancers cured, the cases of spondylitis completely and permanently relieved, the relief given in cerebral palsy, the patients with generalized arthritis deformans brought in on stretchers, and in a few weeks leaving the hospital under their own power.

Medicine cannot cure all patients, neither can Chiropractic, nor Naturopathy, nor Unity, nor Christian Science. You know, and I know you know, that no system of healing has it all. They must unite for the good of humanity and the glory of God. You know that this new racket called Psychiatry is nothing more or less than faith healing. If you keep track of things healing as you should, but apparently do not, or lie, you know that the only men who get any permanent results with these new racketeering tranquilizers are those who *combine pill with prayer, and tender loving care.)*

The next evening when John got home from college, his wife told him that Mother Zollner had been quite indisposed that day and, therefore, had not been able to bake that real bread – German homemade bread. Would he run down to the corner bakery and bring home sour dough bread? He went, but found the bakery closed. The next best thing was to buy a loaf of a commercial bread at a nearby grocery.

When the family sat down to supper, Dr. Zollner looked at the slices suspiciously, picked up a piece, buttered it, and took a bite. "Gott im Himmel, was ist es?" he growled. He often lapsed into German when surprised or angered.

Emilie laughingly replied: "Why, father, that is bread. Mother was too ill to bake, you know I am too busy with the baby to do it. The bakery is closed for some reason, so John ran down and bought this at the grocery store."

John, who by this time was used to real bread, took one bite and laid it aside to poison the pigeons he wanted to get rid of.

They all laughed and ate potatoes, steak, salad and

drank some hot coffee with *pfeffernusse,* that delectable German cookie so highly prized by every gourmand during the holidays.

The following day being Saturday, John took the opportunity to visit the Crerar Library, the world's finest institution for science study. He found that bread – honest, real nutritious bread was composed of good wheat flour, the germ left in, a bit of salt and sugar, water, or milk, fat and yeast. He then went to the library of the A.M.A. and studied the seals of approval given to commercial bakers by an A.M.A. committee. He found baker's commercial bread, in the aggregate, contained many chemicals foreign to bread. As foreign in truth as chalk is to good cheese. He then looked up the matter of the common man's spread, oleomargarine, and found it contained seven chemicals, some of which were under suspicion as being detrimental to health.

(Author: I'll say they are detrimental all, but to cap it all, the butter color was known to be cancer causing, and was made from coal tar. The condition is far worse now, for additional coal tar chemicals have been added to both baker's concoctions and oleomargarine since John began a study of the subject.)

The following Monday, bright and early, John arranged with a biochemist to run a series of tests on commercial white bread, but employing some of Mother Zollner's homemade real bread on another series of white rats. One series of rats were to receive just baker's white bread. The others to receive nothing but Mom Zollner's bread, made from stone ground clean wheat, the germs left in. Both groups got clean water as the only beverage.

(Author: Only the coarser bran was sifted out because, Kellogg and Post to the contrary notwithstanding, coarse bran is an extreme irritant and is condemned by every doctor who has sense enough to pour sand in a rat hole. The best doctor in Mayo's, Dr. Walter Alvarez, declared in print that it was unfit for human consumption, and was nothing but animal food. Bran is just like the rough bark of a tree. But bran has made cereal companies millions in bright, shiny, 48¢ dollars.)

In ten days the group getting the baker's bread made with poison-bleached flour, and five foreign chemicals, was dead. The group of white rats getting the Zollner bread was fat and sassy. Then John really got into the subject with both feet. Healthy puppy dogs were placed on a complete diet, with white, baker's bread fed to six of them. Another six got the same diet with Mom Zollner's homemade bread. In two weeks three pups in group 1 had canine epileptic fits. Every pup in group 2 was in fine shape. A better than average normal gain in weight.

These figures intrigued John, and the bio-chemist, who was a cousin of the greatest bio-chemist in Europe. A cross correspondence was now instituted, and before John's baby was able to say "dada,' the derelictions of government agencies supposed to protect the public against harmful food practices, was positively proved.

John said to Dr. Zollner: "Father Zollner, it tears at my heartstrings to be forced to state, without fear of refutation, that the American People are being systematically and feloniously poisoned en masse."

The doctor showed great concern.

"Let me tell you how this is being accomplished. There are two mammoth dye works in Germany, ostensibly dye works, whose great forte is the production of explosives to destroy humans. There is another war-mongering gang, the Krupps, that has interlocking directorates with the Farbwerke, to make the rifles, cannons and other war material that will use the Farbwerke's explosives.

"But there is even a greater danger and I believe you are far enough advanced in medicine to see the shadow of things to come. I mean those by-products from coal tar and dye operations that are sweeping the world. There is aspirin, antipyrin, acetanalid, salol and a thousand more coal tar synthetics whose use is skyrocketing in

America. Homeopathy, the only true, scientific use of God-given drugs, opposes these poisonous products, and consequently has become *persona ñon grata* with the A.M.A. whose officers have deliberately sold themselves — body and soul to the Farbenfabriken and Farbwerke Hochst. You have already seen the proof of the hatred the A.M.A. and its stepchild, Allopathy, has for Homeopathy and its real scientific medications, in that record I showed you, 'It is better to see a man die under Allopathy, than see him saved by Homeopathy.' But what did you find out about commercial bread and baker's products?"

By this time John had a large brief case filled with the plots of commercial concerns, plus A.M.A. acceptance, plus the coal tar synthetics from German war-mongers.

(Author: May we accept John's offer to read over his shoulder? We may and we shall, and discover the fact that thousands of American political office holders are actually and factually selling our America down the river, and down the drain if not located near a large river. And every statement is made by accepted authorities in their field.)

"Aspirin causes stomach hemorrhage."

"Commerical bread is the 'crutches of death'."

"Hydrolized fats used by bakers, as well as deluded housewives, who have listened to the siren song, are hard to digest. Often cause serious diseases of gastro-intestinal tract."

"No house wife would use such low, filthy grades of flour, as is used in commercial bakeries, in her kitchen."

"Commercial white bread will not sustain life."

"White bread made from degermized, dirty flour is not fit to eat."

"Flour is bleached so the housewife will not know it is made from dirty wheat, well filled with rodent manure and urine."

"Commercial bread contains many chemicals such as propionates, the esthers of propionic acid, bromides, fluorides, borates, coal tar synthetic fats and shortenings, flavors and coloring matters. Commercial baked goods are not safe for human consumption."

"Of the 90,000 deaths yearly from TB in America, 5,000 are caused by eating diseased meat and drinking cow's milk."

"Most hamburgers should be called *harmburgers,* because they are made from meat that ought to be in the garbage can. Sulphur dioxide and sodium sulphate are used to destroy the odor of putrefaction. These sulphur products cause serious gastric and kidney diseases."

"Bran, which has made millions for Post and Kellogg is only fit for animal feed. The human stomach and bowels were not designed to digest coarse cellulose."

"The canned eggs used by bakers in making pastry, is usually a filthy, putrid mass, unfit for human consumption."

"Commercial bread is nothing but a blown-up, pneumatic phoney, and in no way suited for human use."

"We found the eggs full of thermostabile virulent bacteria." (Thermostabile means not destroyed by the heat used in baking.) Furthermore, the de-hydrated egg white, loaded with bacteria, were not heated in preparing frostings." John's records ran into the hundreds. All from reputable sources. And many of the vilest products had the A.M.A. seal of approval! There were, in John's records, proofs that the Food and Drug Administration first condemned bleached flour and later accepted it. Who paid the bill and how much for this treasonable act? The Supreme Court ruled against bleached flour and then the department of agriculture overruled the Supreme Court. These two burlesque bureaucratic blunders permitted the use of poisonous agene in flour and bread for over a third century. And yet the Food and Drug Administration permits the use of poisonous, cancer-producing products to this very day, and at the same time persecutes known cancer curing agents. Just how rotten can men become?

Congress knows of these crimes against the lives of the American citizens. Why don't we wake up? Or have the fluorides, bromides, pro-opinates, coal tar chemicals, so debased and lulled our American common sense until we are not capable of thinking?

The great song "God Bless America" will soon be changed to the key of F (for finis) and scored "God Help America" if we will not think and act. Just a few years ago a wise man said: "When they hanged pirates with chains, in the past, the corpses were let hang until they fell to pieces. This was to serve as an object lesson. What America most needs is ten thousand such hangings in Washington, D.C."

He was righter than rain in a dust storm.

CHAPTER 12

"Patriotism is the last resort of a scoundrel." – Johnson

Have you honest lovers of liberty and our America ever set aside prejudices in Religion and Politics, and for one time actually let yourself think?

Well, one thing is sure: there will soon be no Americans left to think if we citizens do not do some thinking and a lot of acting. A Congressman only recently, when he was in his cups, 'way down deep in 'em, warbled soulfully: "Ninety-eight per cent of Americans have to be fools so we can be elected to make them bigger fools." That brutal, unwise and unjust statement was made by an ultra-crooked U.S. Congressman, who is being paid a salary a hundred times what he is worth. He has been known to use hired thugs to further his political career. He takes extended tours with his family and friends, to Europe, at our expense. His point of call, after he has dodged his family, is the red light houses in the Montmartre district in Paris. And it is said, with considerable evidence to prove the assertion, that he is a sexual and moral pervert.

We Americans today point the finger of shame and scorn at the rowdy Russian Regime, and we are right. But, here is what the Master Christian had to say about such things: "Judge not that ye be not judged." We positively know that the Russian Regime has not kept, and will not keep, a covenant. But did you know that Christian American state and national governments made hundreds of treaties with the real owners of the land, and then broke the treaties into more pieces than Moses did when he broke the tablets of the Commandments? Assume any of us owned a tract of valuable land. Some prospective settler comes over from Europe, likes your property, moves in and takes over. You try to protect your property and your ladies are raped, your sons are slaughtered in cold blood, and you manage to escape; would you not be a little on the misanthropic side?

Before the Pilgrims had been in America a century, they coveted an Indian village of the Pequots. The very people, the Pilgrims, who had left Europe to get away from tyranny, attacked the village, set it in flames, and shot down men, women and children as they tried to escape. A great preacher, who sparked the Salem withcraft murders, one Cotton Mather, wrote in his daily diary: "To see them thus fryinge in ye fire, ye blood quenchynge ye flames thereof, and great was ye stench and ye stynk, but we did consider it a sweet sacryfice, and did glorify God."

This is no idle statement. It is absolute truth and the record is available. (Send for reference, including s.a.e.)

I dare you look up Quakers in the encyclopedia, that is if you are a soul, not a heel. What the pollyanna Puritans did to the Quakers would shame the devil. No Russian rascal ever did worse. I dare you to look up the subject if you are honest and can face facts. We swear and tear our hair at a Bataan Death March, at the inhuman action of the Nazis at the Battle of the Bulge. Be a child of God, be honest with Truth. Look up the Cherokee Death March. I'll give you a hint. The Cherokee Indians had a better culture and literature than the majority of the settlers at Jamestown. The settlers from Europe coveted the lands and drove the Indians off their own property with great slaughter. Later they drove the Indians into Georgia giving them a treaty that granted them the lands they already owned, to be theirs forever and ever. But gold was found in Georgia and agents from the government ordered the Cherokees to vacate their own lands. The Cherokee Council took the matter to the Supreme Court and that judical department decided that the Cherokees did not have to move. But, the government persuaded Andrew Jackson to send in U.S. troops to move the Indians to the malaria-ridden Indian Territory (now Oklahoma). Thousands of the dispossesed Indians died on the march. Some escaped the death march and tried to get back to their own homes in Georgia. They were caught and summarily hanged.

We have the unutterable gall to talk about the Inquisition, the Star Chamber, Bloody Mary, or even that arch-fiend Stalin, or Hitler. I used to see Geronimo at Ft. Sill, a long time ago, and talked with him because I spoke Spanish. He knew how to speak English all right. But the treatment he had received from white Christians was so unspeakably horrible, he would not attempt to use the language of the whites who had slaughtered his mother, his wife and children and hundreds of his friends. The experiences of Cochise, Rain in the Face, Red Cloud, and hundreds more of the only real Americans were equally horrible.

Another instance, among hundreds of them wherein Americans made solemn treaties and broke them at their convenience: the Governor of Colorado made a solemn treaty with the Cheyennes. Within days the American soldiery rushed in slaughtering men, women, and children. These statements are facts that any of us holier-than-thou can readily find, that is, if we dare be honest with God and with ourselves. Did you know that the only treaty Americans ever made with Indians, and kept, was that made by a persecuted sect, the Quakers, under William Penn?

CHAPTER 13

"Who knows a fact and then a falsehood tells
Good men abhor him like ten thousand hells.
— Homer, revised

The last few years have seen the most vicious propaganda against human life that man has ever seen. We speak of mass poisoning, countenanced and apparently approved by agencies in government and medical associations. Nay more, they even launch out against medical agents and treatments that would save more lives than have been lost in war in the last five centuries. The vicious gang, Murder, Inc., were blooming cherubims fluttering around, compared to the operations of the A.M.A. and its dukes in government, as you are about to see.

We but lately called on the person named Larrick, accused by some as being the stoolie for the A.M.A. He does not appear and has sent one of his hatchet men to answer. We will present nothing but facts to this assistant to the assistant chief, listen to any answers he may favor us with, and at all times hold strongly reserved acceptances to his replies. In order to obtain a mildly-reasonable semblance of the truth, we will use Socrates' method of maieumatics.

In these later days it has been the custom to designate all sorts of government activities by the letters of the alphabet – a sort of alphabetical soup nomenclature. There are the XYZ, the PDQ, the DmPHs, and on and on to extinction, or *ad vomitum* to any sensible man. And, too, there is another sort of government chicanery called "top secret," and "no comment." Therefore, in examining a member of the F.D.A. let us use something he is far more familiar with than ordinary common horse sense. Let us use, N.C. for no comment; SOB as Harry Truman used it; T.S. for top secret; N.D.B. for none of your darn business; TH for go to that extremity where all slimy bureaucrats finally take up permanent residence – we hope.

Now then, will person X take the witness stand? We find not a thing in his former personal history to assume that he considers an oath anything but a naughty word; but let the witness beware, for we intend to present the record of his bureau in its very own words and deeds. Person X, you are on the pay roll of the citizens who are examining you, doing nothing of good for your country, or mankind. Is that true?"

"Yes."

"Now, sir, just what do you do of any value whatsoever to the suckers who pay you a rather lush salary?"

"That is T.S."

"Is the person, Larrick, under whom you do no labor, a reputable individual?"

"In confidence, he is a so-and-so. That too is T.S."

"How many moral perverts are in your department?"

"That is strictly N.D.B."

"Is he, in your opinion, Larrick I mean, in collusion with a certain racket to withhold a positive cancer cure from suffering humanity?"

"Yes, of course that SOB . . . hey, strike out that answer. The SOBs would have me crucified if I told one one-hundreth of what I know. My answer is, therefore, N.D.B."

"Now, in your honest opinion, why is it that certain SOBs in your deplorable department give the go-ahead to many known cancer causers, but at the same time make every attempt to prevent known cancer cures from being made available to cancer sufferers sent home to die?"

"Mazuma, and how!"

"What? Do you mean to sit there and testify that those honorable and respectable men would break their oaths of office, and accept bribes?"

"It has been done. But the names of the men who accept bribes, are strictly T.S."

"Are they any more culpable than those that have accepted mink coats, cars, whiskey, jewelry, deep freezers, perfumes?"

"Well, some of the present ruling rulers in government accept only cash at the graveside. Others accept fine livestock, tractors, beaver coats and such. The fact remains that practically every brass collar in Washington would sell his mother into white slavery, to hang on and be what is called a career government employee."

"Does the chief officer of the A.M.A. call at your office? Frequently, that is?"

"The SOB lives in my private office. That should be T.S. but the so-and-so is in my hair and getting on my nerves. Why doesn't he take 'blunder' drugs and drop dead?" Witness keeps his eyes on our 'big black book' and continues: "Say, what is so T.S. about that large book? I hope it is not what I fear it is. I told those skunks that someone with 'guts' would catch up with them." Witness hesitates and testifies further: "Will you promise me immunity from criminal prosecution if I spill the departmental spitoons?" Witness is warned that no immunity can be granted, nor should it be expected. The people have a right to know what government bureaus are doing or not doing.

"You are a lawyer, we presume?"

"Yes, our department is filled with lawyers."

"Do you recall that not very long ago, a U.S. Senator stated that career government bureaucrats ran quite strongly to sex perversions and moral depravity?"

"Yes. But I know many Congressmen, that includes both House and Senate, are that type of vermin. Last year I was sent to France by the head of the F.D.A. to get certain figures, and to try and entice French health officals to permit the importation of American fruits and vegetables that were drenched in poisonous insecticides. Well, Sir, like the large percentage of American government employees, I decided to take in the Montmartre slum district. In some of the rottenest dumps there I saw many Congressmen. There was Senator C........"

"Stop right there, Mr. X. We will call on several of these men to answer for themselves. This 'big black book' contains enough evidence to let them hang themselves, we trust. Now, witness, you admit that the F.D.A. has attempted, under the A.M.A. yoke and threats, to prevent positive cancer cures from being known. Are Larrick and Folsom and other heads of the F.D.A. advised fully about the carcenogenic insectical residuals in all canned goods, dried fruits, bread, butter, margarine, milk, eggs, poultry, in fact, everything we eat and drink?"

"Of course they are. How could they help but know when rabble rousers like you keep hammering and yammering about it?"

"Do those governmental officials in your department admit that diethyl stilbesterol causes cancer?"

"Yes. It is positively known. But, as we have been discussing such matters my mind goes back to the unexpurgated edition of Dean Swift's *Gulliver's Travels.* Have you a copy of it handy?"

There was a copy at hand and it was passed to witness X, who flipped over the pages for a time until he found and read, observing at the same time: "This is the greatest book ever written, after the Bible is excepted. Swift was absolutely psychic, for he describes conditions today better than we who live in this century. Realizing that the heads of most bureaus are lawyers, we read you a bit from Swift. You will then understand the presence of these men in Congress, and heading most departments in U.S. Government:

" 'How many innocent people have been condemned upon the corruption of judges? How many villains have been exalted to highest power, profit, dignity and trust: how many Senates might be challenged by bawds, whores, pimps, parasites and buffoons?"

(Author: Doesn't that describe our present executive, judical and legislative bodies in the U.S. this very day? Were certain judges paid to prevent the positive curing of cancers? Are Senators right this very day refusing to permit the A.M.A. and F.D.A. to be investigated? What other conclusion can we draw from the judicial and executive decisions being handed down?)

The witness, Mr. X. continues reading from the next to the greatest book ever written: " 'They confessed they owed the greatness and wealth to *sodomy and incest; others to the prostituting of their wives and daughters* .... There is a society of men grown up amongst us, bred from their youth in the proving that black is white, and white is black, according as they are paid. To this society all other men are slaves. They have wholly confounded the essence of truth and falsehood, of right and wrong, so that it requires thirty years to decide whether the field left to me by my ancestors for six generations belongs to me, or a stranger three hundred miles off.'

" 'The judge first sends to sound the disposition of those in power, after which he can easily hang or save a criminal, strictly preserving all the forms of the law. . . . Every Senator in the great council of the nation, after he has delivered his opinion, and argued in defense of it, should be obliged to give his vote directly contrary; because if that were done, the result would infallibly terminate in the good of the public.' "

Witness laughs raucously and gives the perfect recipe for making a good legislator, Congressional or State, as follows: *"Ignorance, idleness, and vice are the proper qualities for qualifying a legislator.* Oh, brother, does that man Swift know our government perverts! Thousands of them are in the power of the A.M.A. and Russia because of the knowledge of the two despotisms about sexual aberations and lust."

Witness is ordered to abstain from personalities, and asked if Swift's unexpurgated *Gulliver's Travels* has any light to shed on some Congressional investigating committees.

Witness answers: "Sure he has," and continues the reading of a method to be used by U.S. Congress in illiciting information. He used Swift's own words, therefore, as Swift's *Gulliver's Travels* is not in the least considered indecent or pornographic by the government, let Swift tell the procedure for Congressional Committee. Witness proceeds as follows:

" 'Statesmen, great ones, should examine into the diet of all suspected persons; their times of eating, upon which side they lay in bed; with which hand they wiped their posteriors; to make a strict view of their excrements, and, from their color, the odor, the . . . (Author: Pretty hard to swallow what follows, so on to the next) . . . the consistence, of crudeness or maturity of digestion, form a judgment of their thoughts and designs.' "

Witness is then asked if Swift had any data on organized medicine.

Witness X thumbs Swift's best seller and stops at page 253, which tells a few secrets of the medical monopoly's shortcomings: " 'Therefore, to replace it in the body it must be treated in a method directly contrary, by interchanging the use of each orifice, forcing liquids and solids into the anus, and making evacuations at the mouth. One great excellency of this tribe is their skill in prognostics, wherein they seldom fail; their prediction, in real diseases, generally portending death, which is always in their power when recovery is not; and therefore, upon any unexpected signs of recovery *after they have pronounced their sentence, rather than be accused as false prophets, they know how to approve their sagacity to the public by a seasonable dose.*' "

Witness grins owlishly at his interrogators and quotes from a number of equally condemnatory diatribes against doctors of infamy. "Gentlemen, I believe that the great poet Dryden put that last clause clearly:

" 'He'd rather far that I should die,
Than his prognosis prove a lie.' "

Witness X has made us somewhat nauseated by his

callous attitude, that of a true Washington career man. We are now anxious to conclude his testimony by asking two hypothetical questions as follows: Witness X, we will now ask you two questions. Please wait unto the end of each one before replying. Practically all fresh fruit and vegetables, canned fruit and vegetables, packaged dried fruits and vegetables, all meats, dairy products, bakery goods, eggs and poultry, cola drinks, drinking water, the air, now contain one or more of the following: arsenic, selenium, copper, lead, fluorine, manganese, phosphoric acid, carbolic acid and/or its derivatives, and any one or more of over 2000 highly toxic chemicals. Are any or all of these chemicals under suspicion as cancer causers, hypertension kidney diseases, or diabetes?"

"Yes, it has been positively proved that they are as you describe them – poisonous to the Nth degree. And there are other serious conditions that can be ascribed to them."

"The A.M.A. and the government positively knows these facts. *Why, then, do they not tell the public by press releases to be on page one in every publication in the country? Why do they not placard every post office, as they did a positive cancer cure?"*

"Because they are criminals at heart. Because commercialism is twisting their arms at all times. Because, as Blackstone wrote: 'They are corporations, and corporations do not have souls.' "

(The fact finding body has endeavored to obtain the testimony of one Fishbein. His secretary has reported that he is now on the high seas for an unknown harbor in Senegambia, and that he is not expected to return for many years. This secretary has refused to testify because she fears her testimony might incriminate her, and others in 'an inter-state conspiracy of tremendous porportions.' The exact words pronounced by B. FitzGerald, à government servant of honor.)

CHAPTER 14

JOHN MARSH PRESSING, M.D.

Time passed rapidly over John's head, and dealt very lightly during the time of his college and internship at the Cook County Hospital. He passed his course *cum laude* and members of the profession were courting his friendship with the view to adding this most promising young physician to their staffs just as soon as his two years' service as interne was completed. Many the time his immediate superior, intoxicated when he had commenced a hazardous exploratory laparatomy, and, too drunk to finish the job, had been forced to retire, leaving John to finish the job. More than one of the hospital staff physicians and surgeons were drug addicts and despite the fact that their criminal mal-practice killed many poor patients, they remained on the staff, protected by the medical society.

John noted that patients without friend or means were being used in what amounted to human vivisection — medical experiments. Agents for large pharmaceutical and vaccine houses, seeing in John a successful doctor who might be of service in guinea-pigging their products on unfortunate, penniless patients, courted his favor. They got little encouragement and finally the thing came to a showdown. The book, *That Man Bundesen,* had fallen into John's hands and he had literally devoured it mentally.

One day John was summoned to North Dearborn for what was called an important conference. He was informed in cold turkey terms that he must join the A.M.A., or else. Warned many times by his Dad, Dr. Pressing and by Dr. Emil Zollner, John had for almost the whole term of medical course, and internship, been keeping documented evidence and duplicate sets of notes. At this conference, the member of the medical society put the cards on the table. "If you do not join the A.M.A. and become one of us, we will go to the State Board of Medical Examiners and see that you will never get a license to practice medicine in Illinois."

John smiled as one having unseen, unappreciated powers, and said in the soft voice that men who knew him best, feared to hear: "So that's the way it is, is it?" There were three fairly healthy looking doctors in the room, men who idled on the golf course, calling that exercise, but all of them were flabby and had abdomens with every appearance of pregnancy, when seen in a woman. "Now, I'll tell you some news. I've evidence sufficient to send you to prison. Evidence against medical shysters that I have been collecting for several years. But I have a still more powerful persuader, this –" he shot out his right hand and closed it on a certain section of one doctor's neck, as Kuwo, the Jap *ju-jitsu* expert had taught him. The doctor groaned like one in torment for the simple reason that he was in torment.

John continued his little lesson: "Now, my dear medical pirates, I will get my licensure, or all three of you will know much you do not know, and it won't be from Gray's Anatomy." He released his hold on the officer of the medical association, remarking smilingly the while: "Old Josh Billings once said: 'When you fool with a fool, be sure you have a fool to fool with.' I have evidence in duplicate, stored in places you can never find, that proves that indigent patients are used as human guinea pigs and die in agony. I have evidence that indigent folks in many of the Chicago hospitals are permitted, without proper medical care, to get pneumonia and die. I have several cases in my records showing that you men operated while you were drunk or under dope, cases you murdered. Let me show you something." John reached into a vest pocket and drew out an object not more than half the size of a package of cigarettes. "This," he said, "is a special camera my father-in-law imported from Germany. It was developed for the use of spies. I have taken many photographs of you and others. One look at those by a jury would send you to the chair. Your features and your actions are perfect in my collection. Whether you make any attempts on me or my family, or whether you do not, as a Disciple of Hippocrates I shall do my duty and turn the evidence and the pictures over to the proper authorities."

The doctor who but lately experienced a simple *ju-jitsu* hold, growled: "Who would believe you against men of our reputation? The *Chicago Tribune* and the Associated Press would flay you alive."

"It may be news to you, friends, but I happen to have a few dollars ahead, and they will be used in printing and distributing broadcasts. There are many honest magazines and papers champing at the bit for such evidence, and will feature it so as to ring louder than the Liberty Bell before it was cracked."

The three false doctors looked at each other, aghast. They would do everything in their power to crush this fool, but there still remained enough of the man, although a minimum quantity, to respect a *real doctor,* and better, a *real* man.

As John opened the door he turned and remarked as casually as if he remarked on the beauty of a Spring morning: "Gentlemen, I trust that all is made clear. Do not make it necessary for me to make a return trip, for I might mess you up a little. Good day, gentlemen. Remember my promise to turn all of this evidence I have collected through many years over to men like my father and father-in-law, who cannot be bought."

John closed the door softly behind him and, after descending in the elevator, turned south on Dearborn and walked toward the Loop. As he reached the corner of Dearborn and Lake he noted one of the oldest wholesale and retail Homeopathic drug stores, and, as if guided by a force beyond his volition, he entered and asked for a catalog and price list of Homeopathic products – real scientific medicines that, if they do not cure they will not kill, or injure the *Vis Naturae Medicatrix*. Inside he encountered Dr. Davis, one of the most reputable doctors in Illinois, both M.D. and Chiropractic who had the reputation of bringing healing to those Allopathy had given up to die. Dr. Davis was accompanied by a tall, muscular man whose face showed he was an outdoors man indeed. He introduced the stranger to John as Gustavus Oberg, the man who had taken millions in bright, shiny gold from the vicinity of the Old Lost Dutchman in the Superstitions near Phoenix, Arizona.

John and Gustavus Oberg eyed each other critically as men to stand by and wish for the pull through Eternity. Gustavus thrust out his hand and gave John's hand a crushing that would have ruined any man who had not learned the art of *ju-jitsu*. John knew just when to relax his hand, and before his bones cracked, he managed to hand a crusher to Gustavus' hand that made him wince.

Gustavus roared with laughter. "Son, my name to my friends is Gullible. You see, John, I was called Gullible because every man I met, including several dozen A.M.A. members, thought I was gullible. I like the name, Friend."

On Dr. Davis' invitation, John accompanied him and Gullible to the office. A friendship like that of David and Jonathan grew up in an hour. Mutual experiences and confidences were exchanged.

On hearing of the threats against John and his all, Gullible uttered a full, round oath. "Son, I am going to back your play to the extent of one million dollars. We already have hundreds of pictures and many recordings of A.M.A. and government rascality and criminality, not to mention hundreds of cases of manslaughter and murder. Doctor, may I use your phone?"

Permission being granted, Gullible called a certain number and in a few moments asked: "That you, Marcus? Good. You remember, of course, the spot we have put the medical association on, equally joined together with government officials. We know that A.M.A. has a pretty slick gang of copy writers. I want you, immediately if not sooner, to get the best copy writer on the map. What's that? Oh, I want him to write a book containing all the evidence we have. And we will add to it some of the most remarkable proofs of rascality and veniality extant in these days of the doctors of infamy.

"Furthermore, I want you to call up Dr. .... at the A.M.A. and tell him that if anything happens to Dr. John Marsh Pressing, I will spend another million in placarding every town in America with the facts. What's that? Cost a lot? Who cares. Go the limit if it breaks me and I have to go back to Arizona and make another try at gold mining. Get busy, amigo. That's all."

* * *

When John left the society office, the three conspirators were as frightened as trapped rats. And a cornered rat is ten times as fierce as a Bengal tiger. It need not surprise anybody to listen in on the same type of plot that was planned against the Brother of all good men, Jesus of Nazareth. On reading John 11:50, we find that the scoundrels in His day plotted a means of killing Jesus secretly, saying: "It is expedient that this man die lest our regime perish."

Various means were discussed by the three medical conspirators as how John could be permanently silenced. They talked of hiring thugs, who, deprived of their dope for days, would kill another Paul to get opiates. They discussed kidnapping John, or his wife and child. Of auto accidents, of actually murdering some of the patients John had served in his capacity of interne. But, like Banquo's ghost, the spectre of the evidence John evidently held in escrow haunted them. They even discussed committing suicide in such a way as to throw the blame on John. And as they wracked their brains for some path out of the Gehenna they had created for themselves, the phone rang. The principal conspirator, like the High Priests of Jesus' day, picked up the phone and answered it hesitatingly. He had a premonition this was bad news, and it was.

"Doctor, this is Marcus. Yes, Marcus, legal adviser for Gullible Gus. I now have another client and he has joined forces with Gullible and Dr. Davis. I just want to warn you that if any unfortunate accident happens to Davis, Gullible, one Dr. John Marsh Pressing, or any of his, or their families, or friends, the country will be literally plastered with placards setting forth the truth about your organization, and government agencies in your pay. Not for one minute will you be out of sight from our men. We have the sworn statements of many clerks in your organization. If you are praying men, I would strongly advise you to obey the Master and pray without ceasing that no harm come to those I have mentioned. Good day, doctor."

* * *

In due time, Dr. John Marsh Pressing received his license to practice medicine and surgery in the State of Illinois. Time after time he was offered bribes in the form of kickbacks and split fees, to turn his surgical cases over to A.M.A. doctors. None of them ever reported why they did not further solicit John. It was observed that one surgeon wore a patch over his left eye for ten days after he called on John. One day, before patients began calling, John's attention was called to a two-page spread in an internationally known magazine, lauding bread of the commercial kind. About this time, the A.M.A. was raising a fund to prevent the sick from obtaining adequate medical services by limiting the number of good medical prospects from matriculating in medical schools, by forcing government agencies to refuse help in establishing and maintaining additional medical schools and public hospitals, unless under the aegis of the A.M.A. board of trustees. Naturally the president of the A.M.A. thought of the one thing every man, woman and child uses — bread. So a deal was made between the baking monopoly and the A.M.A., via its president, Henderson. Skilled advertising copy writers worked themselves into a perfect state of idiocy, and had published in that same magazine, a screed that for pure chicanery, lying, malignant mis-information, holds the world's recessional record.

It showed Henderson's coldly, classical countenance with his personal signature stating that the greatly increased health and well being of the Americans was due to the wonderful baker's creations. A few more individuals bearing the title M.D., and more of them with the title Ph.D., also furnished specious recommendations for baker's concoctions. John had in his escrowed file records of payments made to A.M.A. officials that are absolutely shocking even in these days of rottenness in commercialism, medicine and government. John turned over the evidence to Emilie. The fight had begun.

CHAPTER 15

Random Comments

Doctor Van Dellen, writer for the World's Greatest Newspaper, I note your quasi-sarcastic column of, December 6, 1957, and commend your challenge about getting our rheumatic joints greased by taking cod liver oil orally. You are so right in this particular case. But have a care, Doctor, for I am going to shear off your suspender buttons in regard to other matters. I will use your own writings in The World's Greatest Newspaper to check up on your reliability in charging anybody with quackery, charlatanism or empiricism.

Rheumatism is the world's oldest recorded disease, or symptom of poor metabolism; is it not? For over 3000 years scientific medicine has been employing empiricism, and there are more rheumatic patients per capita than ever known in the world's bloody history. Right or wrong? Scientific medicine has prescribed sheep nanny tea, salicylates, wintergreen, oh, for heaven sake! why list the medicine used by doctors, for a list would require a volume to contain them? And rheumatism increases. Your A.M.A. members gave gold, and sulphur and lately you have been doping the unfortunates, and enriching the beef butchers, with cortisone. Not long since you called attention in The World's Greatest Newspaper to the fact that these hormone products from the abbatoirs did not cure. And you pointed out the extreme hazards in employing those products in cases of arrested, or latent TB. You and I know, and you so stated in the *Tribune,* that practically every citizen has had TB, or will have it. Is the administration of the hormones the cause of the again increasing death rate from TB?

As I look over my file of clippings, headed by your by-line, I note that you said, not long ago, that the results from the use of the 'blunder drugs' were not dependable, or any too safe. In fact, you said on two occasions that the side reactions and the end reactions and the chain reactions were such *that the future of the said drugs was in question.* Man, you said a mouthful! But why have you changed the record? Why arc you again advising the use of these drugs? Did Parke Davis, or Lilly, or Merck get your masters?

Have you ever considered the drugs that scientific medicine has used, abused and relegated to innocuous disuetude during the last century? How about alcresta ipecac, phylacogens, sero-bacterins, bacteriphages, cocoquinine, antipyrine, Fowler's solution, Coley's toxin, and on and on? If they were good enough for scientific medicine to use not very long ago, why are they not used now? You say we have far better diagnostic methods and better remedies nowdays. Fie! If that be true, why the increasing death rate in heart and vascular dieseases; in cancer (a disease that is being cured by those you call quacks, and which your colleagues have entered into a conspiracy to withhold from suffering humanity); strokes, so much in the public mind right now because of Eisenhower's present condition; diabetes, in spite of the "shots" from packing house products, namely insulin, a multi-million-dollar maker for Lilly?

You have stated many times that insecticides are safe when carefully used. Who keeps tab to see that this list of insecticides is used with safety? You know that DDT, dieldrin, parathion, arsenic, selenium, manganese and such like are poisonous. You know, or you should, as spokesman for the A.M.A. and The World's Greatest Newspaper, that all of these poisons are cumulative. As you do not seem to know the meaning of the term cumulative. I will tell you: the word means that small amounts of certain poisons are taken into the system every day – the cockroach poison fluorine ingested in drinking water is one example – without any particular symptoms until that fatal day, and then the accumulated poisons fall on a human being like a ton of brick.

Do you read the A.M.A. journal? Many times – thousands in fact – it points out for the A.M.A. members only, the horrifying situation now existing in our nation. And it also throws the deepest suspicion that perhaps most of these so-called cases of polio that Salk vaccine is supposed to prevent but usually does not, are nothing but DDT poisoning.

The World's Greatest Newspaper prints a short article proving that tobacco and whiskey are the principal etiological factors in some of the great killers, even after excepting a juggernaut driven by some adolescent idiot or by a man with a few drinks under his belt, and then runs whole pages of tobacco and whiskey ads. One might think that the *Tribune* and the A.M.A. Journal had interlocking directorates. Dr. Theodore Van Dellen, you know quite well that *Texas Research*, a non-profit research association, found DDT in everything it picked up from markets from Amarillo to Houston, Texas, and in toxic amount. *Texas Research* also found that all vegetation picked up DDT and carried it through to animal and human hosts.

You know that all those hydrocarbon chlorides are cumulative, and probable cancer producers. Yet, in your column you point out the safety of insecticides when, as you state, they are most carefully used. But tell us who does that in view of the findings of *Texas Research*? Did you know that many orchards have well over a hundred pounds of DDT to the acre in the top soil? That winds will scatter DDT far and wide? That there are enormous quantities of DDT in cranberry bogs?

Didn't you read Rep. Delaney's, *Peril On Your Food Shelf?* Various bills have been introduced in Congress over the last 40 years to limit the poisons being poured into food, drink and air. Crooks in Congress apparently sold out to the poisoners! A real man, Representative Keefe from Wisconsin, did his very best despite the A.M.A. and government men in many departments, to get a bill through eliminating coal tar products from anything in the dietary line.

Representative Jim Delaney then became chairman of the committee, and reported and put in print that the growing, catastrophic increase in mental disease may be directly attributed to the introduction, *secundum artem*, into all

man or beast consumes. Delaney calls attention to the foreign-to-food corruptives now used universally as preservers, emulsifiers, blenders, softeners, bleachers, insect and fungus killers, and crop and animal false stimulators. Delaney tells us about the use of fluoric acid, stilbesterol (a cancer caker). Do you know, doctor, that one of the really high class oncologists in the States stated that he picked up chickens in the New York market that contained 342,000 time the amount of stilbesterol to produce cancer in test animals? Think of that! And yet you have written that these food adulterants are safe.

That's a pretty rank situation you must agree, or do you? Delaney tells of the poison in bakers' goods, including the crutches of death, known, in saner and happier days before the A.M.A. took over government food control as the Staff of Life. May we not pause for a moment of prayer: "Lord, give us this day our daily bread but grant that in some way, known only to thy Divine Wisdom, the healthy body you gave us at birth may synthesize some antidote to the propionates, the bromides, the benzoates, the indigesttible synthetic substitutes made from coal tar, full cousins to the anti-freeze in our cars, poly-oxy-ethylene monostearate et cet. Amen."

ADDENDA

The Government admits that less than 50% of inductees can pass easy examinations for military service. The U.N. medical council states that the United States stands 16th in health, and 10th in longevity; that post operative deaths in the U.S. are the highest of any civilized nation on earth.

Henderson and his fellows brag about the abounding health of the American public because of its lush living on lifeless loaves. Hot off the wire:

Dr. J. D. Nichols said before 75 doctors at Behrens Memorial Hospital, Glendale, California that the U.S. had more good doctors, more educational facilities, more great scientists than any country on earth. Nevertheless, said the good doctor, he did not know a single person who did not have some physical complaint. Furthermore, during 1956 we had more cancers, more heart deaths, more high blood pressure cases, more gastric ulcers, more diabetes, more rhuematic cases, and more mental illnesses than any period in our history.

Officials in FDA and USDA have announced that stilbesterol, now used in poultry, cattle and swine in enormous quantities, is perfectly safe. *Stilbesterol causes cancer.* It is admitted by honest researchers. One of the foremost cancer specialists on earth, Dr. W. E. Smith, Harvard Medical School, Rockefeller Research, and Sloan-Kettering Cancer Research Institute said in 1957 that the use of stilbesterol used to emasculate roosters and to fatten livestock was fraught with *infinite danger.* He also said that he had picked up capons which had been treated with stilbesterol, in the New York market, each capon bearing enough of that pharmaceutical-racketeering F.D.A. and USDA-recommended poison in an amount 342,000 times sufficient to cause mouse cancer.

The F.D.A. is now calling on people who admit Hoxsey and Drochnes-Lazenby had cured cancers in their own families. Their agents threaten the cured Americans with prosecution if they do not deny that they were cured by means not acceptable by medical associations. Sweet land of liberty!

From Daily Press: "Cancer caused by chemicals manufacturers are putting in foods you buy." "F.D.A. certified colors serious health menace." "Mineral oils and parafins cause cancer." "Warning against foods sterilized by radiation, and the use of stilbesterol." "Butter colors are condemned because of possible cancer stimulation." "Pasteurization destroys value of milk."

Ten honorable, reputable Doctors of Medicine recommend the Hoxsey treatment for cancer. Thirty regular MDs condemn the A.M.A. radium radiation and surgical methods of treating cancer. The Cancer Societies go along with medical associations. X-rays cause cancer. How about your X-ray gadgets, G.E.?

Radioactive strontium and manganese increased 300% in two years despite the lies from Washington.

From Annals of the N.Y. Academy of Sciences: "Synthetic sugars like glucose, dextrose, corn sugar prevent assimilation of calcium and *help cancer to enter. Milk is pasteurized to hide filthy sources, and admixture of stale returned milk with fresh milk. Price maintained by racketeering practices to rob consumer of wealth and health.* Meats sold in open market are treated with nitrites to maintain color. Nitrites are *poison.* Cancer due to food deficiencies. Every medical doctor who has attempted to give this warning to his patients has been kicked downstairs." By whom?

The report from N.Y. Academy of Sciences continues: "No part of the cancer funds contributed by the public are now used to discover *the fact that cancer is caused by malnutrition. Chemicalized foods are the true cause of polio.* News collecting services cooperate with so-called polio research foundations in suppressing these facts. Not a penny of your donated funds goes to discover the fact that insecticides and possible malnutrition are the cause of susceptibility."

When are we going to stop this idiotic party voting, and vote for men who will re-open the hearing into the rascality of the F.D.A. and the A.M.A.?

Dr. Carlson, a brilliant and honest instructor at the Chicago University Medical School, expressed the theory that the agenized flour bread that the USDA had accepted as safe was the cause of the monumental increase in insanity. Dr. Clive McCay, Cornell University, alarmed by the awful health decline due to eating baker's bread, and who discovered and reported that all cola drinks were slow poison, made up a bread formula that *was* bread.

In 1952 the F.D.A., the organization that has persecuted known cancer cures, ruled that bread, made under McCay's formula was too good and therefore could not be shipped in interstate commerce. The bread was too good!

ACCUSATION

The American Medical Association is a corporation operated for profit. Corporations do not have souls. Ergo the A.M.A. is soul-less.

The A.M.A. has conspired, according to about the only honest government man in Washington, to deprive humanity of treatments that saves lives and intolerable suffering.

FitzGerald points to the conspiracy existing between A.M.A. and sworn officials in a government bureau – the F.D.A.

There is not the slightest doubt that the smoking of tobacco causes cancers, Buergher's disease, accentuates all heart diseases, irritates hypertensive states, and fearfully shortens human life.

The A.M.A. admits this. F.D.A. knows it *and neither of them takes any reparative action.* Why did Eisenhower stop smoking?

The F.D.A. knows that every single substance that humans consume, or breathe, contains cancer-stimulating substances. In fact this agency does admit all these things. But its reports, costing citizens ten of millions of dollars, never reach the great unwashed, the name agents in government apply to us who pay them.

The A.M.A. also admits these crimes and makes mild reports in its Journal. The Journal – a commercial house organ, is never seen by the great unwashed – we who do the weeping, the paying, the bleeding and the dying.

Possibly the greatest of prevaricating parasites in government is the A.E.C. (Atomic Energy Commission). The personnel positively knows and has admitted by voice and in print that atomic fission and fusion is productive of harmful substances in our atmosphere. They have admitted there would soon be not enough places on earth to hide the by-products of atomic fission and fusion even from the production of atomic power. They admitted that all radiation from fission and fusion is cancer producing. They have but lately tried a new tack and stated they have a new hell-bomb that does not give off radioactive substances. But before eating and drinking, this bureau stated many times that it was subjecting the whole country to *a calculated risk of universal extinction.*

Thus continues the siren song to lull us calculated riskees back to sleep. It would most difficult, indeed, to calculate which of our government bureaus can lie faster and more facetiously – and criminally. These statements, fellow passengers to extinction, are 100% factual and documented. Any Washington agent that says anything contrary is a liar. And I can prove it by their own meandering, lying, falacious, health and life-destroying open statements. There is no more dangerous menace on earth than the U.S. Congress that has for nearly half a century known of the castrophic effects now visited on the people through the commercial introduction of coal tar chemicals into everything we use. Eisenhower doesn't drink fluorine water. Why?

Dr. Wiley, one of the very honest and honorable Washington officials, told of this German Dye Cartel in 1903. His country thanked him by having him discharged from office without cause.

Every Congressman positively knows of the speeches made in the House in 1949 by Representative Frank Keefe, denouncing the poisons shot into our foods. Congress has done nothing. Therefore, there is no way of escaping the positive conclusion that a large proportion of our legislative bodies are in the pay, one way or another, of makers of poisons for the mass poisoning of the American people. Fine stock? Furs? Machinery? Deepfreezes?

The news-gathering agencies stock out newspapers with malignant sophistries, and we readers say: "It's all true, because I saw it in the papers, or heard it on TV or the radio."

The F.D.A. knows that tobacco and hard liquors are prime causes of the catastrophic increase in cancer, heart diseases, kidney diseases, mental diseases, and other killers. Nevertheless, the F.D.A. smiles on the things that are ruining the country, and turning us over to Communism, through our own misdirected beliefs in the sanctity of government agents' false oaths; and, at the behest of the A.M.A., persecutes *known cancer treatments that cure cancer.*

Jesus of Nazareth said: "If you forgive not your enemies, your heavenly Father will not forgive you." The million-dollar jackpot question is this: "How can we forgive the traitors who are destroying our country, our families, civilization?"

During 1957, two of the brazen bureaucrats in the F.D.A. have tooted their trumpets as follows: Folsom, a fallout from the Eastman Kodak monopoly, says the mass poisoning must continue until a dastardly Congress gives him a law with teeth in it. (Did Congress give him a law to persecuate a man for curing cancers?) Folsom said it would take two years to run tests on the known poisons already in our foods. In the meantime, hundreds of new, untested poisons are being added every year. This man and his agents have an immediate means of stopping mass poisoning: *Give press releases naming the known poisons in foods, names of products and makers!*

The same year, Larrick, working under Folsom, said it would take seven years to test the known food additives already introduced into our foods. (Query: why don't Folsom and leaky Larrick get together on their data?)

Larrick gave an interview to a Capper publication stating that as we had been subjected to many of these poisons in foods for a considerable time, it was proof that there had been no deleterious after-effects to the people. Doesn't Larrick ever read the records? Doesn't he know that every day less and less people are reaching the Biblical three score and ten? Washington health bureaucrats may deny this statement, and in so doing consign themselves to a few degrees more of hell fire. Even Fishbein admitted that fact, and I have his writings to prove it. Was that why Fishbein got kicked downstairs on a big pension to shut his mouth? And, too, I have statements from his own colleagues that this is absolutely true.

It was a dark day in this country's history when a chief executive publicly hugged and lauded an A.M.A. doctor because of his vaccine supposed to prevent polio. It was a darker day when the great serum plants started out with an insufficiently tested shot for so-called Asiatic Flu. There is no such disease. The real Flu, Spanish Flu, did not yield to pus-punching. Quinine salicylate, phenacetion and salon, plus spiritus frumenti, ad lib. cleared up that disease.

Larrick announced that the potassium iodide in Hoxsey's positive cancer cure tended to produce, or stimulate cancers. Move out, Satan, you're an amateur. We *all* get potassium iodide in vitamin tablets; we get it in iodized salt; potassium iodide is the one best remedy – safe remedy – for syphilis! It is the best drug for use in brain clots. Like what happened to Eisenhower. It is the one thing to prevent nearly all thyroid diseases. And, nevertheless, Larrick persecutes known discoverers of positive cancer cures, on this weird concept, and permits a thousand patent medicines, well charged with dangerous products, to be dinned into our ears and superconscious minds by press, radio and TV.

If Larrick and all his governmental henchmen had one tenth the honesty of Billy the Kid, they would give press releases, and insist that these releases appear on page one. They would go on the air, tell the known facts about commercialism, and warn the public it was standing on a rotten banana peeling, one foot hanging over a newly dug en masse grave. They will not do this. However, there is a remedy that we citizens and voters can use and get results.

Retire every official in political power. I mean every one. Stop voting for party. Start right at the bottom and vote men in who will make public confessions and oaths that they will right the wrongs, or retire on demand. Drop the "Ex post facto," for public officials who have conspired for our downfall. Try political crooks, career officials, and such like for treason. Demand and get an 'Initiative and Referendum' law.

It is already too late to help this generation. It would take ten years to put a stop to food poisoning. But most of us all have descendants. Can we face, dare we bear the fact, that we are sentencing millions unborn to disease, agony and early death?

Let's act now to save the world from our own selfish, crawfishing inanition. Never forget that the sin of omission is on a par with the sin of commission!

Demand full investigation of these horrible conditions, and a complete correction at once!

It's your lives and health, and your children's lives and health.

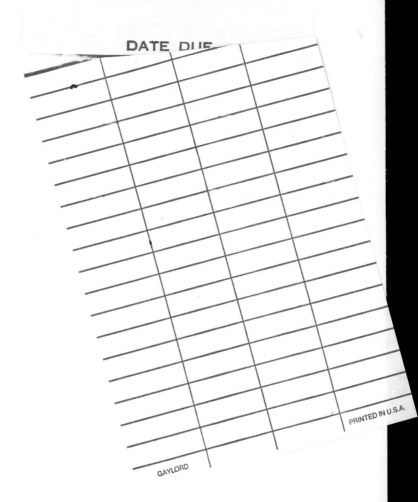